Informed Consent
in Medical Therapy
and Research

Bernard Barber

Rutgers University Press
New Brunswick, New Jersey

Library of Congress Cataloging in Publication Data

Barber, Bernard.
   Informed consent in medical therapy and research.

   Bibliography: p.
   Includes index.
   1. Physician and patient. 2. Informed consent
(Medical law) I. Title.
R727.3.B34   610.69'6   79–20665
ISBN 0–8135–0889–4

Informed Consent in Medical Therapy and Research

By the same author

Science and the Social Order, 1952
Social Stratification, 1957
The Sociology of Science, 1962 (Ed., with Walter Hirsch)
European Social Class: Stability and Change, 1965 (Ed., with Elinor G. Barber)
Drugs and Society, 1967
L. J. Henderson on the Social System, 1970 (Ed.)
Stability and Social Change, 1971 (Ed., with Alex Inkeles)
Research on Human Subjects: Problems of Social Control in Medical Experimentation, 1973 (With John J. Lally, Julia Loughlin Makarushka, and Daniel Sullivan)
Medical Ethics and Social Change, 1978 (Ed.)

To the memory of
Talcott Parsons

Contents

Acknowledgments **ix**

1 The Problem and the Approach **1**
   The Individualistic Error 6
   The Psychological Error 7
   The Communication Error 8
   The Cognitive Error 9
   The Error of the Impossibility of Real Consent 10

2 Values, Norms, and Informed Consent **14**
   Some General Values and Norms 18
   Equality and Related Values and Norms 18
   Individualism and Autonomy 22
   Science and Rationality 24
   The Problem of Trust 27
   Professional Codes and Changing Medical Values and Norms 28

3 Legal Principles, Legal Rules, and Informed Consent **31**
   Principles and Rules in Therapy 35
   Principles and Rules in Research 41
   Changes and Proposed Changes 45
   The Law's Limits 49

4 Authority, Power, and Informed Consent **50**
   Authority and Power in Social Systems and Relationships 51

Authority and Power Patterns in Medical Relationships 53
Some Evidence on Authority and Power Patterns 61

5 Communication and Informed Consent **76**
   Some Functions and Dilemmas of Communication 77
   The Accessibility of Physicians and Researchers 85
   Vocabularies of Illness 86
   Compliance Studies 91
   Physician Awareness of Patient Concerns 99
   Giving the Patient His Record 101
   Communication and Consent in Medical Research 106
   Suggested Improvements in Consent Procedures 115
   Deception in Medical Research 119

6 Socialization, Social Control, and Informed Consent **122**
   Medical Students and Informed Consent 123
   Informed Consent in Internships and Residencies 127
   Informal Mechanisms of Social Control 129
   Formal Mechanisms of Social Control 135
   Medical Malpractice Again 152

7 Informed Consent and Special Populations **154**
   Prisoners and Informed Consent 155
   Children and Informed Consent 166
   The Mentally Infirm and Informed Consent 177

8 Themes and Social Contexts **185**
   Control and Responsibility in the Powerful Professions 187
   Some Recurring Medical and Social Dilemmas 188
   Medical Ethics and Social Change 190

   References **191**

   Index **204**

Acknowledgments

It is a pleasure to acknowledge help from several sources in writing this book. For subsidy of some time released for research and writing, I am indebted to the Population Office of the Ford Foundation and its head, Dr. Oscar Harkavy. Over the past fifteen years, I have learned much from serving on the Drug Research Board of the National Research Council; the Health Advisory Board of the Office of Technology Assessment, United States Congress; the Human Subjects Research and Biohazards Safety committees of Columbia University; and as ethical consultant to the Population Office of the Ford Foundation. Finally, for help received in working on this book and related research over the past several years, I am happy to thank the following friends: Elinor Barber, Connie Budelis, Frank Grad, Bradford Gray, John Lally, Sheila MacLean, Julie Makarushka, Stanley Reiser, Priscilla Schaff, Eleanor Singer, and Daniel Sullivan.

1

The Problem
and
the Approach

We are all now aware that the unethical use of human subjects in biomedical research is a social problem. During the last thirty years—with increasing intensity as time passed—this new problem has been brought to our attention by the German war criminals' trials, by newspaper and television reports of other scandals, by alarmed moral philosophers, by professional self-criticism, by careful sociological research, by university bioethics institutes and similar organizations, and finally by the establishment of the National Commission for the Protection of the Human Subjects of Biomedical and Behavioral Research in the federal government. (On the German war criminals' trials, see Katz, ed., 1972, pp. 292–306: Katz is a useful encyclopedia of primary materials and analysis on medical research ethics. On legislative hearings held by Senator Kennedy to investigate the Tuskegee syphilis experiment scandals, see U.S. Senate, 1973; for an excellent account by a historian, see Brandt, 1978. For the views of moral philosophers, see Jonas, 1969; Ramsey, 1970; and Fletcher, 1973. For professional self-criticism, see Beecher, 1966; 1968; 1969; 1970. For sociological research, see Barber et al., 1973; Barber, ed., 1978; Gray, 1975a; 1975b; Gray, Cooke, and Tannenbaum, 1978; and Mellinger, 1976; 1978. For products of university and other bioethics institutes, see Reich, ed., 1978; the various publications of the Hastings Institute cited frequently hereafter; and the various publications of the National Commission for the Protection of Human Subjects.)

A *social problem,* as social scientists think of it, is not just some readily and objectively observable malfunction of some part of the social system. What is defined as a malfunction of society at one time or place is somewhat variable. Poverty was not always considered a social problem in the sense it now is, nor indeed was the unethical use of human subjects in biomedical research. A social problem is some social condition that a sizable group comes to define as both bad and unnecessary and improvable or removable. In this sense, the treatment of human subjects in research, which many people formerly considered ethical, has come to be regarded as unethical and as a social problem. Many voices, both private and public, now judge certain research practices to be bad and call for reform.

These voices speak in the name of larger social values, reflecting this age of the citizen and of civil rights. We live in a new world of growing aspirations for comprehensive social equality. Complaints against certain established practices in medical research and therapy appeal to these values. They also speak of other, more "realistic" factors, matters of "interest," as we say, such as the increased risk of injury to subjects and patients from the greatly enlarged amount of biomedical research that has become an essential part of the health system during the last fifty years.

Not all voices agree that the present treatment of medical patients and research subjects is a social problem. Even when people agree on larger social values, especially in their most generalized formulations, they may differ about more specific applications of those values. For example, not all who believe in equality, pure and simple, believe in pure and simple equality for women, or blacks, or patients. Social problems thus often involve value conflicts and associated conflicts of interest and power. The new values, interests, and political demands of one group in a society—those who now see some social condition as a social problem—often propose unwelcome costs and political and value challenges to other groups in the society. At several points in later chapters we shall look at these conflict consequences of the new social problem of how patients and subjects are treated. (On social problems, see Merton, 1978; Rule, 1978; and Gaylin et al., eds., 1978.)

Two interrelated evils are defined as the essence of this new social problem: one is the use of research subjects without their voluntary and informed consent; the other is the use of research subjects in experiments where probable risks or probable injuries to the subjects exceed the probable benefits. The nature of these two evils requires some clarification. When we speak of the risk–benefit ratios, as all the regulatory codes of ethics for biomedical research now do, we are referring to the two dimensions of *amount* and *probability* of injury to what we may call "the biological person." In calculating a risk–benefit ratio, we want to know the degree and likelihood of both injury and benefit that will result for the functioning organism. The degree may vary from none or minimal to death; the likelihood may vary from very small to very large. Clearly there are many different kinds of injuries that research interventions can cause in "the biological person." (For further on risk–benefit, see Levine, 1978a.)

When we speak of the other evil, that having to do with voluntary and informed consent, we have a different kind of harmful consequence in mind. Here we are thinking of the degree and possibility of injury to what we may call "the social or moral person." In assessing the degree of informed consent in a research experiment procedure, we want to know whether the study will injure the autonomy and moral integrity of the subject or whether it will cause him to be frightened, embarrassed, humiliated, or hurt in his social reputation. Those who protest against the use of certain kinds of deception in social and psychological research have the same kinds of moral injury in mind as those who protest against the unknowing subject in biomedical research: his moral autonomy is thereby diminished. In our society, that is an injury to the social or moral person.

Thus biomedical research can cause injury to both the biological and the social persons, sometimes to just one, sometimes to the other, and sometimes to both. The matter is further complicated by the fact that the line between the biological and social persons is often unclear and somewhat changeable. We can see this when we consider some of the recent moral controversy over the treatment of fetuses and brain-dead people like Karen Quinlan. In each case, much of the controversy has to do with different assumptions about whether these are only biological persons or also social and moral persons.

In any and all pieces of biomedical research, both issues are necessarily involved because in principle harm in either respect is possible. Decisions about the morality of any experiment usually involve weighing each type of harm separately and then balancing the weights against one another. It should be noted that *weighing* solely refers to a variety of kinds of measures, not solely to some strict and precise quantitative measure. Where such quantitative measures are lacking, and they are lacking more frequently than not, those who do the weighing are required only to do the best they can. Experience and prudence are often sufficient guides where precise quantitative measurement is impossible.

The outcomes of balancing the weights of the injury and consent issues with one another are varied, complex and of different relative morality. A low risk–high benefit–full informed consent combination is obviously moral. Usually a high risk–high benefit–full consent combination is also considered moral. By contrast, some would judge that even a low risk–high benefit–no informed consent combination is immoral, a judgment that clearly puts great emphasis on injury to the social person. This was the judgment in the Southam-Mandel scandal, when live cancer cells were injected into geriatric patients without their informed consent. (On this case, see full details in Katz, ed., 1972, pp. 9–65.) Even though the risk of causing cancer was minimal, those who protested were morally outraged by the lack of consent. And to show how important consent is morally, there are some who would say that where consent exists, even if there is high risk and not much certainty about the benefit, subjects and experimenters should be allowed to proceed.

In this book, we are concerned with the issue of informed consent. Though the risk–benefit issue is also important, as we have seen in examining the various ways it combines with consent, it is the latter that seems to have the greater weight and moral priority. The Christian ethicist, Paul Ramsey, who has specialized recently in the study of medical ethics, has remarked that " 'no consent' rather than 'no risk' or 'no discernible risk' is the decisive point at law and in the morality govern-ing medical research" (1970, p. 700). Injury to the social person is of more concern to people than injury to the biological per-son. Indeed it may be that biological injury is of concern only insofar as it is defined as having consequences for the social person and his ability to function. Meaning and morality are of the essence of being human. Another moral philosopher, John Fletcher, who has written and practiced in the field of medical ethics, stresses that what he calls "personhood" and the con-sent that must go with it are the central concerns of the ethics of medical research (1973). Another philosopher, Robert Veatch, in a paper prepared for the National Commission for the Protection of the Human Subjects of Biomedical and Behavioral Research, also argues the priority of the moral right of "self-determination" or "autonomy" as the basic element in all codes of ethics for patients and subjects: the "right to consent [is] not derived from the notion of risk to the subject" (1978, p. 17). It is an independent and prior moral principle. Veatch points out how "uniquely modern" this principle is as an explicit right; it is a product of general value changes that have occurred in modern Western society since the eighteenth century, particu-larly in our postwar world.

We now have some research evidence comparing the ways the public actually weighs or combines injury to the biological per-son and informed consent and the priority the public assigns to consent over risk–benefit issues. Preliminary findings have been reported, from a study still in progress, of the public's views on these matters. Glen Mellinger and Mitchell Balter have obtained these views by presenting small samples of the public with con-crete and specific vignettes describing experimental research situations of varying degrees of possible injury and varying amounts of consent. They find that when consent is present the public is willing to tolerate fairly high possibilities of injury to the biological person. They describe this willingness as "a generally permissive stance." In contrast, the public feels strictly about the necessity for informed consent. The authors report that "the majority of our respondents believed that informed consent and permission were necessary in all of the vignettes we presented, except in the case of using anonymous computerized records" (Mellinger, 1976, p. 51). They add that a sizable majority "took the position that informed consent was necessary *even though the placebo would do no more than deprive subjects of a vitamin that was described as probably ineffective!"* (Mellinger, 1976, p. 51; authors' emphasis). Even for a urine test that involved essentially no risk to subjects, a sizable majority of respondents in this pilot study felt that informed consent was necessary. This emphasis on the essential nature of informed consent is "in striking contrast to the generally permissive stance these respondents adopted with respect to condoning research that puts subjects at relatively high risk" (Mellinger, 1976, p. 51). Remember that respondents condoned such practices only when informed consent was present.

As might be expected from the scope of current moral and legal concern with the problem of informed consent, a great deal has been written about it. A recent National Library of Medicine bibliography of writings that deal with informed consent in some fashion covers only the period from May 1974 through June 1976, but includes 403 citations (N.L.M. Literature Search No. 76–35; this is an "update" of L.S. No. 74–16). Nearly all this material lacks systematic analysis and good data. Whether speaking for liberal or conservative positions, writing about informed consent is likely to be characterized primarily by moralizing and prejudice. We need to know much more about informed consent and we need to know what a social systems analysis and good data can tell us. Social problems are almost never immediately and easily solved by such analysis and data; but with them we have a better chance to devise workable and morally desirable amelioration.

To the sociologist coming to the literature on informed consent in the hope of applying a social systems analysis, a number of serious errors in search of correction quickly become apparent. These basic errors are pervasive and recurrent and make satisfactory analysis impossible. Here are some of them: though they are interrelated and often occur together, they are discussed here one by one for purposes of greater emphasis and clarity.

THE INDIVIDUALISTIC ERROR

This error consists of defining informed consent as the outcome of a transaction that occurs between two, and only two, individuals—the physician and his patient or subject. But more is involved than these two individuals. The medical care and research system is a complex multiperson system in which two individuals are or might be influenced powerfully by a variety of other persons. The doctor has been influenced in his values and practices with respect to informed consent by his teachers and other role-models, by his colleagues, by the public (through its values and norms), by his more remote professional associates (through the rules they formulate in his professional associations), by the nurses who assist him, by paramedicals, and by the rule-setting administrative officers of his hospital or other medical practice group when he works in such a setting. As for the patient, he is influenced by his family, his friends, by members of what Eliot Freidson has called his "lay-referral" group, by the nurses or other paramedicals who often actually obtain his informed consent, by other patients, and by journalists who define the medical system for him and his rights and obligations in it. We shall not understand informed consent until we look beyond the doctor and patient as two isolated and insulated individuals to the actual structure of the social system by which their behavior dealing with informed consent is in fact determined.

THE PSYCHOLOGICAL ERROR

A common error in writing about informed consent is to see it wholly as the outcome of the personalities of the participants in the process. Research doctors, seeking to explain and explain away delinquencies of their colleagues in obtaining informed consent, attribute such delinquencies to "bad guys," of whom there are said always to be at least a few in any group. "Good guys," "compassionate" doctors, "warm" types do not do such things, they say. (See Barber, 1976; and Lally and Barber, 1974.) Similarly, from the psychological perspective, troubles with research subjects in the process of informed consent are alleged to occur because subjects are "frightened," or "overly aggressive," or "suspicious." While personality is always one important determinant of behavior, and while personality characteristics are in part responsible for some of the defects of the process of informed consent, they are still only one part of the picture. The multiperson, multidimensional social system in which particular personalities participate is a powerful influence on actual behavioral outcomes. Indeed, so-called personality characteristics either are often the direct results of social systems or can be effectively controlled by them. "Bad guy" or "insensitive" medical researchers could be educated by their teachers or colleagues into "good guy" behavior, or such behavior could be eliminated or reduced by a variety of effective social controls from the professional community or from outside regulatory agencies. As for "frightened" patients, they might become informed and willing subjects if the social system of medical research provided them with helpful nurses, social workers, or even physician patient-advocates. (On the patient-advocate, see Annas and Healey, 1974.) It is often the real social system that is frightening them, not some inherent personality characteristic. Conservative medical researchers who wish to avoid making necessary improvements in the present processes of informed consent often display the psychological error. "Human nature is what it is," they are likely to say, offering a rationale for the status quo. Instead of appealing to the supposed eternalities of psychological human nature, however, they should be considering the possibilities for improvement offered by changes in the social system of medical relationships.

THE COMMUNICATION ERROR

This error occurs in many areas of social analysis. There are those who think that management–labor differences, racial or ethnic conflicts, family troubles, and political controversies could be wholly solved by improved communication structures and processes. So it is with discussions of informed consent. A heavy burden is laid at the door of poor communication. It is true, of course, that better communication and better understanding and knowledge among the participants in medical research and care would improve the process of informed consent. In a later chapter, we shall present detailed evidence on some of the defects in the present structures of communication and understanding. But good communication is not enough. Patients, physicians, and other participants need to use certain values and norms to define what constitutes proper and sufficient communication among them. We need better basic and continuing education for all parties on how and what to communicate. There have to be better social control mechanisms to see that impediments to effective communication are removed and communication errors are corrected or made inoperative. Even with the best communication imaginable, problems remain. Participants in the medical care and research system share many goals and values, but they often have different emphases within these values. They also have some different goals, values, and interests. Scientists care more about science than laymen do. Physicians and patients and their families do not always agree about how to proceed, for example, how to treat, with therapy or research, the dying patient (Crane, 1975). Even where there is excellent communication, problems remain, problems that have to be resolved or accommodated by a variety of other social, moral, legal, or political processes. Communication structures and processes are only one part of a social system.

THE COGNITIVE ERROR

This error often accompanies the communication error. It assumes that the only important thing in the process of informed consent is the cognitive understanding among the participants, the degree to which they share and communicate valid, objective, rational, and scientific knowledge. The process of informed consent, however, must consist of a structure of supportive values, emotions, and ideologies as well as one of relative cognitive understanding. "Enough" cognitive knowledge or "valid" scientific knowledge is always relative to a structure of values that determines what is enough in the light of the possibilities of existing knowledge and of the other exigencies of the situation of action. Especially so far as informed consent to medical research is concerned—where knowledge is often partial, where consequences may be somewhat uncertain—a set of values and the exigencies of medical care may suggest a smaller or less valid amount of cognitive knowledge than would be prudent in other social situations as a "prudent" basis for taking action. Neither doctors nor their patients and subjects can afford to insist upon the fullest imaginable realization of cognitive understanding. Beyond some prudent sufficiency, there is room for shared values, for trust, and even for expectant hope.

THE ERROR OF
THE IMPOSSIBILITY OF
REAL CONSENT

Among those who are resistant to changes in the process of informed consent, who are conservative about the status quo in medical research practice, there is much recourse to this erroneous argument. Real consent on the part of the subject is impossible, they say, because he or she cannot ever really understand the technical substance and methodology of a research experiment. Only the experimenter himself can do that, and perhaps a few of his colleagues who sit on the peer review committee, although even that may be doubtful. An expression of this error in the *Journal of the American Medical Association* calls informed consent "a legalistic fiction that destroys good patient care and paralyzes the conscientious physician. It hedges the experimental situation with barriers that cannot be surmounted. It is not applicable, even by definition, to a large segment of the involved population. The term has no place in the lexicon of medicine. The integrity of the physician continues to represent the most effective guarantee of the rights of the patient and of the experimental subject." The author realizes, however, that all is not well in the present situation, for he continues, "for this to remain valid, the medical profession must augment its concern for the moral values of its members" (Laforet, 1976, p. 1582).

Indeed, much is of considerable substantive and methodological technicality in any scientific experiment, but some effort can often translate this into terms of relative amounts of risk that the layman can understand well enough to make a prudent decision for his own welfare. That is all that the law and morality require of the researcher. They do not require some utopian, impossible, unreal consent process. In the real and morally satisfactory world, informed consent is a matter of more rather than less, of better rather than worse, of the search for improvement rather than of the commitment to formalized and inadequate consent.

With good data and good social systems analysis, all five of these common obstructive errors can be corrected. In the chapters that follow, we shall be doing this. We shall look at the values and norms, the legal principles and rules, the communication structures and patterns of understanding and misunderstanding, the authority relations, and the contexts of informal and formal social control that determine the relations among the many participants in the medical research system and result in better or worse processes of informed consent. With our social systems analysis, we shall look at a multiperson, multidimensional system in which both indirect and direct effects occur with unintended as well as intended outcomes. Such a social systems analysis, grounded on data as good as are available, should give us a more accurate account of informed consent and should provide a better basis for the policy and procedural recommendations we shall discuss throughout the book.

Here, at the end of this brief introduction to what we shall be about, a few other special characteristics of the book may be noted, and some we have already mentioned may usefully be reemphasized and clarified.

First, we should note that although the title mentions both medical therapy and research, we shall be concerned somewhat more with informed consent in research. (We shall not here be concerned with problems of informed consent in connection with national immunization programs, problems partly similar to, partly different from those in the therapy and research contexts. For a discussion of consent in the context of the immunization program, see National Immunization Work Groups, 1977.) However, many of the values and legal principles, the social and role contexts, the problems and processes, are the same in both situations; and we shall therefore need to attend to both. Although many Ph.D.s are now involved in medical research, indeed many researchers now have both M.D. and Ph.D. degrees, the key role in medical research using human subjects is played by the M.D., the physician, and so consent to research cannot be separated from therapy. (On the difficulties that patients have in separating research from treatment, see Lidz, 1977.)

Second, although we shall have no large concern for the processes of informed consent in social research, once again we find that many of the processes and problems are the same. Where knowledge about informed consent in social research, especially in psychological research, can shed light on the medical situation, we shall use that knowledge.

Third, in discussing informed consent in medical research, we shall frequently have occasion to refer to the special privileges, immunities, powers, and obligations that medical researchers possess as recognized and prestigious professionals. As professionals, they are similar in privileges and powers to such other professionals as lawyers, priests, and academics. The social control of the powerful professions, all the professions, is currently the topic of considerable discussion. (See Barber, 1978–1979; Auerbach, 1976; Berlant, 1975.) Wherever it can be illuminating, in either data or analysis, we shall refer back and forth among the medical profession and the other professions.

Fourth, wherever possible—we want to reemphasize—we shall explore the significance of the best available systematic data and research evidence on the several dimensions of the medical research system. Good knowledge always tends to be in short supply when social problems first come into view. So it is in this case. But such knowledge is essential, if not always sufficient, for understanding and improving the system. For example, what does research evidence tell us about just how frequently procedures of informed consent are present when research is carried out? We need to know this basic fact before we know the size of the social problem. Just how satisfactory are the procedures that are used in these cases? We also need to know that fact to know the size of the problem. In addition to reporting what the research data tell us, we shall try to indicate the limits of the data and where good data are badly needed.

Finally, we need to amplify what we mean by our intention, throughout the book, to consider various recommendations for policy and procedural changes. In considering such recommendations, we are mindful of the fact that social change in complex social systems is neither easy nor likely to be quick. Social change is hard because it is often not so much a process of extirpating a single radical evil as of accommodating competing and equally important values and interests to one another (Rule, 1978). For example, inadequate informed consent in medical research requires us to accommodate the needs of scientific progress with the conditions for maintaining the moral worth of individual subjects. We also need to be mindful of the unintended social consequences of policy changes; there are side-effects in both social systems and human organisms. We shall also keep in view the fact that when social problems exist, when we have the social conflict that necessarily attends them, we often find overreactions and overreaching in the name of one important interest or value as opposed to some other equally important one. Though they have their place, moral absolutism and moral outrage are often poor instruments for obtaining rational remedies. We shall be on guard against futile moral outrage from either researchers or subjects. We shall look for rational remedies as we consider policies for change.

2

Values, Norms, and Informed Consent

We can begin by taking values and norms together as one essential determining variable in consent processes in the social system of medical research and therapy. We
begin here not because this variable is the most important—no
single essential variable in a system is in principle more important than the others; that is the nature of a system—but because
a great deal of the existing literature recognizes and emphasizes
values and norms. We think we can add something in the way of
analysis and data to this discussion. Social problems, as we
have already said, are always, in considerable part, value or
moral problems—the results of changing and conflicting values
and norms in different parts of a social system's membership.
This is certainly true, as we shall see, with present concerns over
the nature of what should be proper informed consent in medical research and therapy.

First, we need some definitions, specifications, and delimita-
tions of values and norms and their effects on social behavior.
The first question we must answer is that of why we should
choose values and norms. Human social action and social sys-

tems are processes of choice among various necessary, desirable, and valued alternatives. Indeed, it is an essential characteristic of human action, in comparison with the behavior of nonhuman species, that it involves choice among some alternatives, which although they always appear to be definitely limited, are made possible by human culture. Choice, whether explicit or not—and much of it is unwitting rather than explicit—is ubiquitous and continuous in social systems. As a result, the values and norms that express the patterned principles of these choices are equally ubiquitous and continuous.

The problems of choice and of the values and norms that emerge to guide them arise around all the functional exigencies of human action. To subsist better or less well, to treat one's fellows equally or unequally, to fight wars or not to fight them, to search actively for healing remedies or to suffer passively and die early, to give time and other resources to people who think about the meaning of life or to people who can produce more food or better houses, all these and many others are the kinds of choices societies and their members endlessly make—for which they develop those preferred patterns of choice we call values and norms. Thus in the most general and comprehensive way, human action involves a structure of differential evaluation of alternatives. In the specific case of medical research and therapy, human action involves a structure of values and norms expressing differential evaluation of alternative procedures for such key issues as informed consent and the risk–benefit ratio. At the present time, our evidence seems to show that we are experiencing a change in the values about procedures of informed consent. We are moving toward an enlargement and strengthening of those values and norms that express preference for more satisfactory procedures of informed consent.

Values and norms in general, and the specific new values and norms for informed consent, affect our everyday behavior. But their effect, it must be stressed immediately, is always limited. Some moral philosophers, experts in the study of values and their applications to concrete social situations, forget this and absolutize one or another value or values in general. The same tendency often affects the rest of us when we become excited about one value or another: we tend to forget about other elements of the social system and their constraints. We tend to absolutize our values, although values are limited in their effects in at least two different ways.

First, since there are many dilemmas and choice-points in any social system, we do not have single values but sets of values for the different dilemmas. Although there is usually considerable congruence among the different values and norms, each has its special sphere in which it sets limits to the values for other spheres. For example, we value equality highly: we feel that every human being should be treated the same. But we also value the special solidarities, the special modes of treatment, for those of our immediate kin, or our clan, or our nation. Although the two values are both important to us and we strive to maximize each of them in such a way as not to restrain the other, they nevertheless do so. We see the same thing in the area of informed consent. We value full disclosure, so that the subject or patient can make a reasoned and prudent decision for himself; but we also value the humane protection of those who are somehow weak or inept—the young, the frightened, the dying. In some situations, the two values limit one another; and we can only devise accommodations to this limitation. For example, in the realm of medical therapy, one accommodation is the longstanding right known as "the therapeutic privilege," that is, the right of a physician to decide not to tell something to his patient when he judges that witholding this information is in the patient's best interest. It is interesting to note that the New York State Board of Regents, in judging Drs. Southam and Mandel for injecting live cancer cells into geriatric patients without obtaining their informed consent, decided that this physician's right did not hold in medical research situations. The regents decided that only protection of the weak rather than the needs of science justified limiting the value of informed consent (Katz, ed., 1972, Chap. 1). We should not conclude from this that the value of science could never limit the value of informed consent. No value is an absolute. Later on, we shall explore some of the ways in which science may put some limits on informed consent and how the two need to be accommodated to one another. Informed consent is no more an absolute than any other value or norm. Daniel Robinson has made a convincing legal and moral argument that there can be and is what he calls "legitimate coercion" in society, that in both therapy and research there are grounds for state action that limit informed consent (1974). For a long time, Alan Westin has been concerned with the dilemmas posed by the value we place on the individual's right to privacy and the value we place on the society's need to know some essential things about all individuals (1967). How these values need to be, have been, and can still be better accommodated to one another has been the continuing focus of his analysis and research (Westin, 1972). Finally, and perhaps most directly relevant to our purposes, we should note that when the National Commission for the Protection of Human Subjects of Biomedical and Behavioral Research recently took up its legislative mandate to set forth a set of basic "ethical guidelines and principles" for the protection of human subjects, it defined a set of three such prescriptive and generalized norms—respect for persons, beneficence, and justice—and emphasized the way in which these three interact with and limit one another (1978c).

Besides being limited by one another, values are further limited by a variety of social structural requirements and conditions found in a social system. Although we value equality highly, social systems often require differential authority, that is, some inequality in the socially structured right to make decisions for families, for patients, for organizations, for states, for a whole variety of collectivities. In Chapter 4, we shall examine the patterns of authority in medical research and therapy systems and see what limitations they may place on equality and informed consent. To take one more example, the capacity to realize the value of informed consent is constrained by the socially structured distribution of knowledge and understanding among both physicians and patients. We shall explore the relationships and accommodations among these two elements in Chapter 5. Values, other cultural elements, and social structural requirements and conditions always create complex interrelationships that both facilitate and limit. We must always look to the limits as well as the facilitations.

One last word of definition before we proceed to discuss some of the values and norms relevant to informed consent. We have referred several times to *values* and *norms* without distinguishing between them or explaining the significance of the distinction. *Values* are meant to refer to the *more general* patterned principles of choice in human action and *norms* to the *less general*. Values and their more specific norms tend to be arranged in hierarchies, the values at the peak and the norms underlying them and applying them to a variety of specific social groups and situations. Thus the general value of equality is at the peak of a hierarchy in which there may be norms of equality for sexes, different ethnic groups, age groups, and doctors and patients. Values and norms maintain a dynamic relation with one another. A general value may be called on to legitimate an established norm or a desired new norm. Those who propose new norms for informed consent in medical research and therapy appeal to such general values as equality, autonomy, human dignity, and altruism. Those who hold a value intensely may actively search for new specific contexts in which it can be applied in the form of new norms. Thus the more general moral stances interact with the less general. Those who resist specific norm changes, such as equality for women, may resist or resent this fact of interaction; but it is one of the determining factors in all value and norm change and stability.

SOME GENERAL VALUES AND NORMS

We come now to our discussion of some of the values and norms especially relevant to the problem of informed consent, although we must remember that neither social analysis of value systems nor research in this area is settled and highly developed. (For the best statement on theory and research on values, see Williams, 1971.) Our discussion is intended to show the importance of some selected values, not to be the final word.

EQUALITY AND RELATED VALUES AND NORMS

Central to the set of values relevant to informed consent is equality. As a value of the highest generality, it has a pervasive influence in our society, affecting every institutional and cultural sphere. Its roots extend deeply into the basic Judeo–Christian beliefs about the "children of God." In secular ideology, our beliefs in the "brotherhood of man" underlie our commitment to equality. The great eighteenth-century American and French revolutions established equality as one of our premier values. A history of Western society, and indeed all of human society since then, could be written as a history of the struggle to realize the value of equality in more spheres of life and more fully in all those spheres.

Recently there has been much talk of "a revolution of value expectations," one essential part of which is a demand for greater equality. In comparison with the longer, larger equality revolution that has continued for the last two hundred years, this new revolution is only a small perturbation. Nonetheless, there does seem to have been a significant rise in expectations for equality in the short run in recent years, and in our present short run it is a significant social and cultural movement. The movement includes a wide variety of demands for more equality from many different social groups and categories who feel they have not been treated as equally as they might be and want to be. Thus we see blacks demanding greater equality from whites, women from men, young from old, students from teachers, poor from rich, patients from doctors, and subjects from biomedical and social researchers. In the last two cases, an essential part of the demand is the call for better procedures of informed consent in therapy and research.

In a national sample survey carried out by the Harris Poll in 1973, 78 percent of the respondents agreed that "every patient should be told the full extent of his illness and dangers, as well as the help he might receive from certain kinds of treatment"; 74 percent felt that "any patient should be able to refuse treatment or medication even if it is strongly recommended by a hospital." So much for people's feelings about informed consent and rights to make decisions in the therapeutic situation. They are even stronger in regard to the medical research situation. By a nearly unanimous 97 percent, the national sample agreed with the statement that "no patient should be experimented on by doctors without the patient's permission and a full explanation from the doctor" (Harris Poll, reported in the *New York Post,* April 23, 1973).

Sometimes these demands for equality overlap. Thus not only do women protest unequal treatment from men, but women patients complain about the superior attitudes of male doctors. These complaints and a call for new norms in this area were expressed at an annual clinical meeting of the American College of Obstetricians and Gynecologists. Dr. Valerie Jorgenson of the University of Pennsylvania Medical School warned her colleagues, both men and women, that the Woman's Movement has produced a new generation of women who are expecting and demanding "new attitudes" from their physicians. (*Medical Tribune,* June 11, 1973. Another expression of this demand can be found in a widely sold publication, *Our Bodies Ourselves: A Book by and for Women,* by The Boston Women's Health Book Collective, N.Y.: Simon and Schuster, 1973.) Dr. Jorgensen said that women were tired of "medical omnicompetence" and want to be "informed and educated." They want to "participate and share in reaching health decisions." Physicians "have neither the right nor the responsibility to decide" by themselves for their women patients. Dr. Jorgensen speaks of an "active role" for women, of their helping themselves to equality through their "peer groups" if their doctors do not help them. She emphasizes that women want to be "partners" in the medical relationship. All this is a vivid and concrete specification of new equality norms that women will increasingly expect from physicians and researchers. (For a report on a research study on some fifty women who were not well informed about the research in which they participated, see Gray, 1975a.)

Because we do not have a standardized vocabulary for our values, we find that the same value may sometimes be phrased in different ways. This seems to be the case for the values placed upon equality and human dignity. Human dignity is another way of saying equality, not so much by explicitly comparing any one individual to one or more others but by leaving the comparison implicit. When we speak of the moral claims of human dignity, we say that each individual in and of himself deserves to be treated in a certain way, with respect and protectiveness. We do not mean that each individual is unique, but rather that he shares certain moral rights equally with every other human individual by virtue of being human. The assumption that equality can be left implicit places an emphasis on the value of human dignity in such a way that it may be taken as the ultimate expression of the importance of equality. Certainly, phrasing in terms of human dignity is common in discussions of medical ethics and informed consent. In whatever phrasing, it is one of the values most relevant to these ethical problems.

Another value closely related to equality is altruism. When all men and women are valued as equal, then what Talcott Parsons has called "universalism" prevails (1954, pp. 34–49). Benjamin Nelson has described how this value and its significance for altruism evolved in Western morality: "In short, Western morality after Calvin reaffirmed the vocabulary of universalism, refused to concede that God could authorize or equity allow us to treat the Other differently from the Brother, assimilated the Brother to the Other, and eventuated in the Universal Otherhood" (1969, p. xxv). In his book on blood donation, the English sociologist, Titmuss, has expressed the same value. Because all men are equals and brothers, they owe each other the altruistic gift of blood, not for money payment, which would be immoral, but as a free gift because all men are equal (1971). Applying the general value more specifically to the area of research on human subjects, Freund has spoken of "the voluntary community," and James has said that "the right to informed consent must, therefore, increasingly be accompanied by the development of strong public opinion for the responsibilities of the present citizen toward his colleagues of tomorrow" (Freund, 1969, p. 318; James, 1970, p. 304). Thus it has become increasingly clear that when more equal treatment for patients and subjects in therapy and research exists, there will be a stronger value expectation that reciprocity and altruism will prevail, that patients and subjects will have the moral obligation (when properly informed) to serve others besides themselves through their willing participation in medical teaching and research. The equality that leads to better informed consent will also lead to more altruism in medical systems.

Does the medical profession accept the norm of medical altruism to the extent that it might? Speaking from their experience with kidney donors, Drs. Fellner and Schwartz have deplored "the distrust and suspicion with which the medical profession regards the volunteer donor and his motivation. This distrust and suspicion reaches major proportions in the genetically unrelated donor, often unacquainted with the recipient, who wants to volunteer" (1971, p. 283). As evidence of this distrust, they report not only public expressions against it from distinguished physicians working in the area but also disapproval of the use of such donors by the majority of fifty-four kidney transplant centers. They feel that there is much altruism in the general public and that it should be respected by the medical profession. For example, they point out that eighty-five people answered a plea for a kidney to be used in a transplant in Cleveland in 1963. They ask, "Does such willingness to be a donor reflect psychopathology, or could it reflect healthy altruism derived from genuine moral concern?" To help answer their question, they designed a study that obtained written questionnaire responses from 116 adults chosen to be representative of the population of a small Midwestern city. Their data showed that "a substantial proportion of the public, especially among the young and well educated, consider the use of living transplants—even for saving strangers—to be a reasonable procedure and one for which they might themselves volunteer." As further evidence of public altruism, Fellner and Schwartz refer to a Gallup Poll (January 1968) in which over 70 percent of the public expressed willingness to donate their hearts or other vital organs to medical science upon death. They recognize, in regard to their own study as well as the poll, that responses to hypothetical questions are not necessarily the same as actual behavior. Still, they feel that physicians and researchers should know more about the distribution of altruism in the population and respond to it in ways other than distrust and suspicion. (For some other small studies of medical altruism through questionnaire responses, see Martin et al., 1968; and Arnold, Martin, and Boyer, 1970.) Going even further than Fellner and Schwartz, but reasoning on the same grounds, Fost has said that even children down to the age of seven years should be used as altruistic donors of kidneys (Fost, 1977). In an editorial, in the same issue of the *Journal,* Hollenberg argues against using children in this way.

INDIVIDUALISM AND AUTONOMY

Individualism and autonomy are another pair of related general values that will strongly affect the actual practice of informed consent in medical research and therapy. These are values for nearly all situations and nearly all persons in our society. In the medical situation, they apply not only to physicians and researchers but also to subjects and patients. Where individualism applies to all categories of participants in a social system, it follows that new claims for more of the value from one category may be seen by those in the other categories as encroachments on their established and legitimate claims. So it is now in medical research and therapy. New claims for more individualized treatment, for more autonomy, by patients and subjects are seen as threats to the stable moral order by some physicians and researchers.

First by social and self-selection, then by their training both in medical schools and in internships and residencies, and finally by the structure of medical practice, physicians engaging primarily in therapy are strongly pushed toward and become committed to the value of individualism (Freidson, 1970, pp. 60, 63–77). Selection processes for medical training emphasize the value of the strong, striving, independent individual. This value ideal is strengthened in medical school itself and in postgraduate training because the role-models there are the "star" scientific and clinical performers who have gained their peak positions by exceptionally strong individual achievements. Finally, when the mature physician goes out into practice, he is typically on his own, either in private practice or as part of a group practice or a hospital staff where he is left to himself by his colleagues. Steeped in individualism, the physician naturally resists standards set by outsiders, whether they are medical peers, patients, private or public bureaucrats, or government legislators. In our time, the American Medical Association has been as much a sacred repository of individualism as the American Chamber of Commerce. Modern physicians have not been trained to share (nor do they believe in sharing) autonomy with their patients. (See Carlton, 1978.) They consider demands from patients for more information or for the right to consent subversive of a stable and morally proper order of things.

As for medical researchers, they display all the individualism and autonomy of therapists and add to those values the prerogatives of those who strive to be creative and original scientists. Their goal is to conduct research on their own terms. They too are impatient or contemptuous of calls for informed consent from their peers, their subjects, or government regulations. Correct moral behavior, they feel, comes only from "the integrity of the individual." This was the position taken by Dr. Henry Beecher in recommending remedies for the delinquencies of colleagues who did not obtain proper informed consent or undertook studies with unfavorable risk–benefit ratios (1966,

p. 1135). Researchers were either good individuals or bad individuals, and there was no awareness of the fact that they were being educated and controlled by a social system into what their subjects and the public were now coming to think of as morally bad individuals. The strong force of medical individualism will not easily be reduced by the value changes occurring in our time.

As for patients and subjects, even when they expect themselves to be strong in other social contexts, they typically become passive and dependent in the medical situation. They do not insist on their rights to information and decision as they do in other contexts. When they do, as we have seen women now doing, they do so with some of the exaggeration, uneasiness, and stridency that often occurs among those who seek to change established moral orders. It is often no easier for patients and subjects to demand moral and social change than it is for physicians and medical researchers to accept it. Patients who value individualism in general and who have learned to live by its norms in other contexts are trying to establish a new norm for its application in the medical situation.

SCIENCE AND RATIONALITY

Ever since the seminal work of Max Weber, social scientists and humanist observers have agreed on the central importance of the values of rationality and science in modern society. The value of rationality consists in the moral approval of the critical approach to *all* the phenomena of human existence in the attempt to reduce them to ever more consistent, orderly, and generalized forms of understanding. The value of science, which is relatively speaking a little more specific than rationality and therefore perhaps one of its norms, consists in applying rationality to the empirical world: physical, biological, and social.

We do not have satisfactory data on the actual distribution of the values of rationality and science in the general public. We observe widespread rationality and use of science in actual behavior, but our direct studies of these values need to be considerably extended. (For a summary of what we do know about the distribution of the value of science, see Etzioni and Nunn,

1974.) Lately, as research funds for basic science have been decreasing while public questions about the ethical aspects of science and medicine have been increasing, some scientists have accused the general public of "antiscientism," of a flight from the values of science and rationality (Graubard, ed., 1978). It is true that the public in general seems to value science more as an instrumentality, as a means to the good things of life, than as a good in itself, as scientists themselves value it (Etzioni and Nunn, 1974). But data from public opinion polls and survey research do not support the allegation of antiscientism. For example, Etzioni and Nunn point out that in a Harris poll carried out in 1973 asking the public to express the amount of confidence it felt in sixteen different institutional areas of American society, science ranked second (along with education), and medicine, which is not without its strong scientific component, ranked first (Etzioni and Nunn, 1974, pp. 195–200). On the basis of evidence produced from three different sources, first, a specially commissioned national sample public opinion survey; second, a consultative panel of professional experts; and, third, a colloquium of experts, the National Commission for the Protection of Human Subjects concluded as follows about the attitudes of Americans toward biomedical science:

> In general, these different approaches yielded similar results. The immediate consequences of the scientific and technological advances in biomedical and behavioral research and services since World War II are perceived, for the most part, as beneficial by professionals and lay public. . . . among all of the Commission's respondents, no significant body of opinion emerged that was opposed to continuation of the scientific and technological research that has led to so many innovations since 1945 (1978e, pp. 5–6).

The public is ambivalent about science, as it is about all values when it is translating them into real life, for in real life other values and a variety of social conditions interact with any one single value to produce some ambivalence.

When we move away from the general public to that part of it made up of medical practitioners and researchers, we find a somewhat different picture. There—especially during the last fifty years when there was an ever-increasing amount of basic medical science to value—science has been held in the highest esteem, partly for its instrumental use in therapy and partly as an end in itself, especially for basic biomedical science researchers. Dr. Gray Dimond, provost for health sciences at the University of Missouri, a leader in medical education, has discussed the heavy weighting on science and science ability in American medical schools during the recent past. "In reviewing applicants for medical school, admission committees have given preponderant attention to college (before medical school) grades in science. High achievement in the science score in the Medical College Aptitude Test (MCAT) became a favored index" (1974, p. 1118). Moreover, Dimond says that the medical school faculties have rejected the role of physician as practitioner and emphasized the role of physician as scientist and researcher: "The faculty, in fact, has to a major extent sought to replicate itself," he says, by heavily science-oriented curricula, by offering themselves as the best role-models, and by rewarding those students who showed most aptitude for joining the scientific elite (1974, p. 1118). Dr. Dimond is asking his medical colleagues to reduce their emphasis on science for its own sake in the interest of greater concern with primary care for patients. Others have asked for the same reduction in the interest of giving more "freedom and equality" to their patients and subjects (Branson, 1976). Neither request is hostile to science. Both are asking only for a redress of the balance between science and other values and interests.

Not only for their students but also for their colleagues, the heroes on many medical school faculties have come to be the innovative research scientists. "In this country, as well as in others," Dr. Henry Beecher has said, "medical schools are dominated by investigators. In the last two or three decades, few if any individuals in the leading schools have achieved professorships until they have proved themselves productive in research" (1968, pp. 150–151). For such medical professors, science became a value more important than any other. Research became more important than the ethics of research or of such matters as informed consent. When Barber and his colleagues asked a sample of 350 medical researchers, "What three characteristics do you most want to know about another researcher before entering into a collaborative relationship with him?" 86 percent of the respondents mentioned scientific ability, 45 percent mentioned motivation to work hard, and 43 percent mentioned personality. Only 6 percent mentioned anything that could be classified as "ethical concern for subjects" (Barber et al., 1973).

The medical researcher's commitment to the value of science is nowhere more dramatically manifested than in the practice of autoexperimentation, which has a long history in medicine. One physician, who has made himself an amateur historian of this practice, has found in his not altogether exhaustive readings some 137 cases of autoexperimentation involving more than 185 investigators (Altman, 1972). His references span four centuries and include several examples from the 1970s. It is, he says, "a rather common means of contemporary investigation." It has been used in all the subspecialties of medical research. Those who have used autoexperimentation have given as justifications for its use "convenience, availability, simplified schedules, time-saving, elimination of the need of explanation ('informed consent'), etc." Altman recognizes, however, as have other physicians commenting on this practice, that the researcher's willingness to use autoexperimentation is no justification for not getting informed consent from others he uses as subjects. (See, for example, Blumgart, 1969, p. 260.) Those who would make themselves martyrs for science have no moral right to treat others in the same way.

THE PROBLEM OF TRUST

One of the values medical therapists and physicians consider important for their successful performance is the value of trust (Freidson, 1970, pp. 119–121). This value refers to the willingness or "faith" that their patients and subjects should have not only in their competence but also in their devotion to the welfare of those they serve. Lately there have been many voices in the medical world deploring the decline of the public's faith and trust in them.

Trust is a characteristic of social relationships that are either stable and satisfactory or satisfactorily changing in the right direction for *all* participants. Trust is likely to decline where shared values are breaking down or where there are emergent values in some members of a social system not shared by others. This seems to be the case in medical therapy and research at the present time. Patients and subjects want more equality, more participation, more informed consent; doctors and researchers favor the status quo, want to maintain established values, and resist or resent the changes asked of them. Trust will be restored or strengthened only when patients and subjects are convinced that physicians and researchers share and act upon the new values. The actual satisfactory use of more practices based on informed consent is what patients and subjects want, not requests to place unsupported trust in their doctors' "integrity as individuals," which is a frequent shibboleth among those who deplore the decline of public trust.

PROFESSIONAL CODES AND CHANGING MEDICAL VALUES AND NORMS

One place where we can look for evidence of changing medical values and norms is in the professional codes medical men have constructed since Hippocratic times to define morally proper relationships with their patients. We should remember, of course, that such codes are expressions of values and norms that influence but do not wholly determine their actual behavior. We should perhaps also note, as an indicator of the long-established superiority of the profession over its clients, that professional codes have been constructed almost entirely by physicians themselves, with little or no participation by laymen, though such participation may now be slightly increasing.

For the longest part of their history, professional medical codes have been paternalistically nonegalitarian (Berlant, 1975; see also, Pellegrino, 1976). The Hippocratic Oath required that physicians refuse patients' requests in certain cases, for example, when they requested abortifacients. The oath also stipulated that it is the doctor's right to determine what confidences to keep in his dealings with his patients. So, from the beginning in the practice of medicine, informed consent has not been an accepted norm. The paternalism of medical professional codes was continued in the first great modern code, the one that has influenced nearly all subsequent codes, Percival's *Medical Ethics.* Implicit in this code, in the American Medical Association's first code (1847), which is directly based on it, and in all subsequent codes until quite recently, is the assumption that it is for doctors alone to decide what is right and proper for their patients.

So far as medical therapeutic relationships are concerned, the first expression of more egalitarian values is expressed in the Patient's Bill of Rights, published by the American Hospital Association in 1972. Under the value prescriptions of this code, the physician is no longer the sole authority in managing a case and deciding what to tell the patient and his relatives. The bill of rights says decision making should be shared with the patient and even acknowledges the patient's higher authority for his own welfare in some situations. This code applies, of course, only to patients in hospitals, not to those in doctors' offices or elsewhere. It has not yet been adopted by the American Medical Association for medical practice in general. Nor do we know how effectively the bill of rights has been adopted even in hospitals. There seems to be considerable variation. At one hospital, which has been particularly active in producing a more egalitarian and active role for its patients, the Beth Israel Hospital in Boston, a second edition (1976) of its brochure, "Your Rights As a Patient," has already been issued. The Beth Israel code puts great emphasis on information and informed consent for all patients in all contexts. In contrast to the Beth Israel's strong stand, many hospitals have apparently done nothing. In 1974, some eighteen months after the American Hospital Association published the bill of rights, it reported that only about one-third of the seven thousand hospitals in the country were using the statement "in one form or another, either as a pamphlet or as a plaque on the wall" (New York *Times,* June 16, 1974). However slowly, change is occurring. After nearly two thousand years, some professional codes are now expressing a new equality for the patient.

More equality and more informed consent for the research subject was provided in medical codes somewhat earlier than it was for the patient. Codes for research changed somewhat earlier because of the discovery in 1945 at the end of World War II that Nazi doctors had experimented without their consent on prisoners in the concentration camps. As a result of the trial and imprisonment of these doctors, the Nuremberg Code for experimentation on any subjects, which was formulated in 1947, explicitly stated the requirement of informed consent. Many world, national, and professional specialty codes for experimentation have been published since then, and all emphasize the importance of informed consent. (For the Nuremberg Code and a selection of some thirty-nine other codes or variants on codes, see Beecher, 1970, pp. 213–310.) Scandal has always been a powerful impetus to social change, at least so far as public statements of values go.

3

Legal Principles, Legal Rules, and Informed Consent

We have seen that values and norms are patterned principles of choice that can be either implicit or explicit, unwritten or written, maintained by either informal or formal social mechanisms and agencies. Legal principles and rules are different. They are always written and always formulated by some formal agency of social control; and their enforcement is always assigned to some formal body. Thus legislatures make statutory law, courts adjudicate and make legal rules and principles, and administrative bodies make legal rules on the basis of general principles laid down in the relevant statutes. All such types of formal bodies make legal principles and rules for the governance of practices with respect to informed consent. Like values and norms, laws differ in their degree of generality. Legal principles are more general, and legal rules are specific applications of legal principles. As with values and norms, there is also a dynamic relation between legal principles and rules. Legal principles may be applied to new concrete situations to make new legal rules; and those who want new rules for a new social problem may appeal for justification to legal principles. We shall see

31

that both types of dynamic relationship between legal principles and rules have occurred in the case of changes in the laws and practices of informed consent.

Those learned in the principles of the law remind us that law, like values and norms, is a *set* of principles, an interacting system of general legal commitments that are generally consonant but can also set limits to one another. In short, as we have seen to be the case for values, there are no absolutes in the law. Speaking to this point, Professor Paul Freund, a legal theorist and professor of constitutional law, reminds his readers of Justice Holmes's "regular challenge to his law clerks: 'State any proposition, and I'll deny it.' " "The law is dialectic," says Professor Freund. "It mediates most significantly between right and right" (Freund, 1969, p. 314). Although the law has been paying more attention recently to the principle of informed consent, and to strengthening its supports, it has not treated this single principle as an absolute. In this area, the law's main problem is to work out new accommodations between informed consent and other important legal interests and principles. For example, the legal principles of protection of the public interest and the right to free inquiry come into conflict at some points with the principle of informed consent. As Professor Jay Katz has put it in his learned and deeply felt discussion of informed consent and the law, "Anglo-American law is caught up in a conflict between its vision of human beings as autonomous persons and its deference to paternalism, another powerful vision of man's interaction with man. The conflict created by uncertainties about the extent to which individual and social-well-being is better served by encouraging patients' self-determination or supporting physicians' paternalism is the central problem of informed consent" (1977, p. 139). Katz feels that because the weight of legal opinion has so far gone more to the value of medical paternalism than to that of patient self-determination, the strengthening of the principle of informed consent in the law will be hard to achieve. "Medical law in the United States is a clear case of institutionalized paternalism. . . . When judges began to consider the issue of patients' autonomy in medical decision-making, it took place in a climate where the question of self-determination had been neglected by law for centuries" (1977, p. 140).

The question of the relations between values and norms on

the one hand, and legal principles and rules on the other, is often raised. Does one always predominate over the other? How consonant with one another must they be? William Graham Sumner held that mores, or values and norms, make the laws. Others who have studied the matter or who have wished to enact new laws to change old norms (for example, in matters of race relations) have held that laws can change mores, at least under some conditions. We can, they say, get more "equality by statute" (Berger, 1952).

In fact, the relations between values and laws are complex and dynamic. On the whole, the values and laws of a social system have some tendency to be consonant with one another, arising out of common moral roots. This is certainly so in the long run, though in the short run there may be all sorts of inconsistencies, discrepancies, and conflicts. That is inevitable, especially in changing social systems. In situations of change, new values and norms arise in new social situations; and their holders press for their incorporation into and enforcement by statutory, administrative, or judicial law. The law often lags; it contains old principles and rules that no longer have moral support but have not yet been extruded. Sometimes the law is ahead of established values, or at least a minority of the society is successful in making an appeal to some principle of the law for adjudication of a new problem when a majority of the population still has moral objections to seeing it applied. So far as informed consent is concerned, we are certainly in a time of change. As we look at the actual relations between laws and values about informed consent, we must keep all these general complexities in mind if we are to understand what is happening and what is possible.

Social groups differ in their attitudes not only toward specific legal rules but also toward the law in general. Strong groups committed to the value of freedom are likely to be hostile to the law in general as a social control mechanism and to any specific legal rules that they see as restrictive. Weaker groups are likely to look more favorably on the law in general as a source of protection and equity; they welcome specific laws that strengthen their rights to achieve greater equality in competition with stronger groups. The established professions, not least of all the medical profession, have been among the stronger groups, consistently hostile to the law as a mechanism for con-

trolling their behavior. The professions have wanted only minimal legal control over relationships among colleagues and with
their clients. Indeed, as with the state licensure laws of which
they have approved, the professions have gone along with legal
regulation only because the actual administration of these minimal laws was effectively in their control through their domina-
tion of the licensure boards. The professions have strong value
and interest stakes in their own autonomy and self-regulation;
and they resist any change they consider a legal infringement.

Against this general background, then, it is only to be expected that the medical profession, both therapists and researchers, should oppose new laws—whether statutory, administrative, or judicial in origin—that impose controls on their
customary procedures with respect to informed consent. In this
part of their domain, the medical profession has been conservative, wishing to preserve the status quo. It has not been respon-
sive and creative, as it has been in the scientific part of its domain. It has viewed the law as only negative and restrictive when
legal changes have been proposed or enacted. There is a need
for a more positive and creative response from the medical
profession to new laws about informed consent, not only to
acknowledge the new value claims these laws represent but also
to protect more effectively those other legitimate values and
interests the profession seeks to maintain and strengthen.

As we turn now to look at some of the legal principles and
rules that apply to informed consent practices in medical
research and therapy, and as we consider some of the changes
now occurring in this area, we must take note of some essential
facts: it was only yesterday that the law began to pay any attention at all to informed consent. Statutory and administrative law
goes back only to the 1960s; judicial decisions go back a little
further, though also in no great seriousness or volume until recently. We should also remember that the courts thus far have
dealt much more often with problems of informed consent in the
treatment situation than with those in the research situation. It is
the opinion of at least one eminent expert on medical law that
the courts will probably insist on some differentiation between
treatment and research, though we know that the two now often
overlap (Frank Grad, personal communication). It is his opinion
that the courts are likely to differentiate between what they
would see as the more protective physician-therapist and the

more activist, "gung-ho" physician-investigator. In short, we are still in a period of flux and confusion with the law of informed consent. But it is also a period of great opportunity, a time when the law could be used constructively to create a more satisfactory accommodation between the principle of informed consent and the other essential principles of medical therapy and research.

PRINCIPLES AND RULES IN THERAPY

We have said that it was only yesterday that the law began to pay serious attention to the problem of informed consent in medical therapy. (For a detailed review, see Katz, 1977.) In 1969, in a review of the problem, Waltz and Scheuneman commented, "The doctrine of 'informed consent' has achieved a status in the law of medical malpractice unmatched both in speed of growth and bulk of commentary. Physicians, eyeing the lengthening list of cases, have become increasingly concerned about the doctrine. In response, legal writers have been obliging in the number of articles that deal with it" (1969, p. 632). A few years later in one such "obliging" article, a notewriter in the *New York University Law Review* said, "The requirement of informed consent—a patient's right to be knowledgeable about a proposed treatment and to have a meaningful choice whether to submit to that treatment—has recently surfaced as a major issue in litigation and commentary concerning medical malpractice" (Note, 1973). We shall see that this new problem, while now under intensive legal discussion, is still far from settled.

The novelty of the problem of informed consent in the law is in no way more strikingly demonstrated than by the fact that there has never been, and there still is not, an *independent principle* of informed consent in the law. The problem comes up in legal cases now not as a right in itself but as an aspect of the older tort law principle of battery, which has also recently been extended to include negligence. This tort principle holds that every adult has the right to control what happens to his own body, not to be "touched" in any way he or she does not assent to. The integrity of the individual is an important principle of the law. A classic early formulation of the principle was pronounced in 1914 by

Judge Cardozo in *Schloendorff* v. *Society of New York Hospital:*
"Every human being of adult years and sound mind has a right
to determine what shall be done with his own body; and a surgeon who performs an operation without his patient's consent
commits an assault for which he is liable in damages." This
doctrine in the tort laws of battery and negligence was given
even greater specificity in the important 1960 Kansas case,
Natanson v. *Kline:* "[It is] the obligation of a physician to
disclose and explain to the patient in language as simple as
necessary the nature of the ailment, the nature of the proposed
treatment, the probability of success or of alternatives, and
perhaps the risks of unfortunate results and unforeseen conditions within the body."

Thus, while informed consent may be moving slowly toward
becoming an established legal rule, priority in the law still rests
with the issue of injury. The plaintiff must allege and show first,
that he was injured by the treatment; second, that the physician
did not inform him of the reasonably foreseeable risks involved
in the treatment he was to receive; and third, that he would not
have accepted the procedure if he had been adequately informed. The question immediately arises of how the courts
define "adequately," "sufficiently," or "reasonably" informed.
That is where the difficulty now lies for plaintiffs, defendants,
their counsel, and the courts. As we look at current legal actions, we can see that the courts are trying to construct definitions of what would be "sufficient" information not only for "the
average prudent person" but for the specific plaintiff who represents himself as an average prudent person in his particular
case.

At the present time, the courts follow two rules: what the legal
commentators call "the majority rule," followed by the majority
of courts; and "the minority rule," laid down by the minority.
The two rules agree on certain principles and disagree on other
important ones. Both the majority and minority rules agree, for
example, that there are some *limits* to the extent of "sufficiently
informed." Certain risks are so well known to everybody that the
physician is under no obligation to inform his patient further.
Also, both rules agree that certain very general risks inherent in
any procedure, for instance, the risk of some totally unexpected
event, need not be disclosed. The two rules agree further that
there are two legitimate *exceptions* to the obligation to inform

the patient adequately. The first occurs when the patient is unable to consent, for example, an emergency situation with the patient in coma. This does not mean that the physician is given a paternalistic grant to decide because "it is good for him" that the patient does not have the ability to consent. The exception holds only when the patient is in serious danger. One extreme situation where the exception does hold occurs when it is the physician's conviction that the patient will die if he does not accept the treatment. The second established exception to the obligation to inform is the time-honored "therapeutic privilege," that is, the doctor's right, indeed obligation, to withhold some aspect of the patient's diagnosis or prognosis when he considers it to be in the best interests of the patient's health or welfare. The therapeutic privilege rests on the assumption that the physician cares not only for the patient's physiological health but for his psychological and moral well-being. In the interests of the latter, he may choose not to tell him about the former. The burden of proof here would, of course, be on the physician. While there may be dispute over specific instances of the use of the therapeutic privilege, there has been no challenge to its basic function. It is a right of the doctor that serves as one limit on any absolute definition of the principle of informed consent.

So far all courts agree about informed consent. But they now disagree on an essential matter, of who ought to have the greater weight in defining what it is "reasonable" to have the physician disclose to his patient. The majority rule gives greater weight to definitions constructed by the professional medical community; the minority rule says these definitions should not necessarily prevail and asks for definitions that hold in the lay community, the community of ordinary citizens and patients. We might call the majority rule the "reasonable practioner" rule and the minority rule the "reasonable man" rule. This disagreement over whose "reason" is to prevail is at the heart of the present flux and confusion in the courts on problems of informed consent in medical therapy cases.

As we have said, the "reasonable practitioner" rule looks to the medical community for authority. "The majority rule," says one commentator, "compels a physician to disclose facts which a reasonable practitioner in a similar community and of the same school of medical thought would have disclosed to his patient regarding the proposed treatment" (Note, 1973). This puts the burden of proof on the plaintiff—the patient. "Since only doctors are competent to testify about medical customs, majority rule jurisdictions require the plaintiff to introduce expert testimony to establish the doctor's duty to disclose" (Note, 1973). This burden of proof is often difficult for the plaintiff because of the unwillingness of a great many physicians to testify against their colleagues. Indeed, this unwillingness has sometimes been called by bitter critics "a conspiracy of silence," though it is unlikely that any deliberate conspiracy is involved. Moreover, as the recent increase in the number of malpractice suits indicates, there is an increasing availability of medical experts to testify for plaintiffs. In Chapter 6, where we discuss the various mechanisms by which physicians do or do not effectively control one another's behavior, we shall look a little further into this alleged conspiracy of silence and its sources. The fact that the majority rule puts this heavy burden on the plaintiff has come under considerable criticism on the ground that procedures having to do with the right to be informed adequately about medical "intrusions" on the body ought to be decided at least partly by the society at large, and not solely by the established customs of physicians.

This criticism and the dissatisfaction associated with it are, of course, sympathetic to the development of the "reasonable man" rule that has occurred in a minority of jurisdictions. This rule looks to the community at large for authority, not excluding the medical community as a part of the larger community. The minority rule requires disclosure of what it calls "all material information," that is, "information which a reasonable man in the situation which the physician knew or should have known to be the plaintiff's would deem significant in making a decision to undergo the recommended treatment" (Note, 1973). Thus the physician is required to use his knowledge about people in general and his patient in particular to decide what a reasonable person in his patient's situation would think was material in giving his consent to treatment. The physician is required under this rule to know about the values of his patient's community, not just about the values and customs of his own medical colleagues. Under the minority rule, the burden of proof is on the physician. As he takes up this burden, the defendant physician and his counsel may introduce expert testimony, but it does not have the last word. The last word rests with the community at large, as represented in court by the jury. In discussing the shift in legal decisions from the "reasonable practitioner" standard to the "reasonable man" standard, as I have called them here, the philosopher, Robert Veatch, in a paper prepared for the National Commission for the Protection of the Human Subjects of Biomedical and Behavioral Research, says this development is "the most exciting theoretical conceptual shift in the ethical and legal dimensions of medicine in the twentieth century" (1978b, p. 35). He sees that it may also have large implications for change in the nonlegal social control mechanisms for research on human subjects, mechanisms like the institutional review boards.

Recently, however, there has been a certain withdrawal from the "reasonable man" rule. As a result of the so-called "epidemic" of malpractice suits in 1974 and 1975, some twenty states have written new malpractice statutes intended to make such suits harder to institute and win by requiring expert testimony (Frank Grad, personal communication). These statutes have thus strengthened the "reasonable practitioner" standard.

Obviously, although it seeks to change basic standards of legal proof in informed consent cases, the minority rule itself still has considerable shortcomings, at least in its present undeveloped state. As one legal commentator puts it, "the materiality standard fails to apprise physicians adequately concerning which subjects to disclose. Since the rule's ambit is potentially unlimited, the command to divulge all material information exposes doctors to uncertain demands and therefore threatens the rule's efficacy" (Note, 1973). These difficulties and the resulting confusion have been noted by several other commentators. Dr. Samuel D. Rhem, III, a physician and attorney, said at the Twelfth International Conference on Legal Medicine that there is "considerable confusion about which risks are material" (Reported in *Medical Tribune,* June 1972). The American Medical Association has been concerned for its members about this new and dangerous confusion. Richard P. Bergen of the association's legal department has written, "A physician seeking specific guidance on what information he or she should give a patient to obtain 'informed consent' for a particular medical or surgical procedure is confronted by legal confusion. There are at least 17 different rules of law on the question, each of which applies in one or more states. A few states have not, as yet, adopted any rules of law on the subject" (1974, p. 325). Although a member of the office of general counsel of the association has tried to summarize the general principles of the law of informed consent for A.M.A. members (Holder, 1970) and the association has also printed a list of "all reported appellate court decisions" in the matter, on the whole the association seems to have given up on giving specific advice to its members. One of its statements declares: "Therefore, the Office of the General Counsel of the AMA has concluded that it is not possible at this time to develop any universally applicable and specific standards of disclosure that would assure physicians of reasonable protection from legal risks" (Bergen, 1974, p. 325). This seems to be an unnecessarily negative and unconstructive view of the matter. Waltz and Scheuneman, two legal commentators, do agree that "at this juncture, it can be concluded that the set of concepts surrounding the doctrine of informed consent are slippery and complex. Dealing as they do with such broad areas as medical judgment, scientific knowledge and human communication, there can be little wonder that doctors have been concerned and courts have been less than precise" (1969, p. 645). Still, they feel that the "problems are susceptible of rational solution." Professor Frank Grad agrees. He thinks it is easy to exaggerate the uncertainties and difficulties of medical diagnosis and prognosis; physicians could usually know what to do and what to say to the patient (personal communication). As we shall see in Chapter 5, there are serious defects in the training and practice of physicians with regard to satisfactory communication with their patients. Speaking from another point of view, that of legal counsel for physician defendants, Hirsh also agrees: "Even though the law does not have absolutely certain answers, we have seen that there are relatively well-established rules, adequate to provide sufficient practical guidance to enable countless physicians to go about their duties with only rare encounters with legal difficulties" (1970, p. 314).

The negativism of the A.M.A. needs to be replaced by more constructive efforts to clarify what might be some practical and specific guides as to what is material to a patient under the standard upheld by the minority rule, a factor that becomes all the more important as it diffuses through the legal system. In a little while, we shall look at some proposed changes in legal rules and standards that might diminish the present confusion over informed consent in legal proceedings. These changes indicate how the newly emerging legal principle of informed consent can be translated into specific, accessible, and manageable legal rules.

PRINCIPLES AND RULES IN RESEARCH

As is not the case in medical therapy, in medical research the legal principle of informed consent is now established in its own right. Both statutory law and related administrative regulations define informed consent as a primary independent principle for the regulation of research on human subjects. Moreover, considerable success has already been achieved in specifying a set of rules by which the general principle is to be realized in actual research situations. This process is, of course, far from complete. The Department of Health, Education, and Welfare, the local peer review committees which it now requires to approve all research on human subjects, the National Commission for the Protection of Human Subjects, and the Food and Drug Administration, both separately and interacting with one another, are now continuously working at the task of specification to protect both human subjects and the interests of research. In this chapter and throughout the book, we describe these efforts, their successes, and their continuing problems.

Although now an accepted and independent principle for medical research, informed consent is a relatively new development in this area too. Speaking in the late 1960s, one longtime legal observer of the relations between law and medicine, Professor William Curran of the Harvard Medical School, said:

> In the years prior to the current decade, there was little "law" in the United States concerning medical research. There were no specific federal or state statutes purporting to regulate research organizations or investigators in their research methods, their areas of research, or the use of subjects or patients in such work. There were also no reported court actions involving liability issues or criminal actions against research organizations or personnel (1969, p. 544).

One of the few relevant court actions was *Fortner* v. *Koch,* a malpractice action occurring in 1935 in which an innovative therapy was at issue. In this case, the Michigan Supreme Court authorized clinical investigation on new therapies as a legitimate part of medical practice—stipulating, however, that the patient must know about the investigation and consent to it. In the normal course of events, through such court cases as this a law for informed consent in research situations would have been created. As Curran puts it, "the law concerning human experimentation, therefore, could be expected to develop on a case-by-case basis in traditional common law fashion. The courts would look to experts drawn from the research field to testify as to common, accepted practices" (1969, p. 546).

But this was not how it was to be. Action came instead early in the 1960s through federal statutory enactment and through governmental administrative regulation. Probably influenced by nongovernmental codes such as the Nuremberg Code (1947) and the Helsinki Declaration (1961), and also by the thalidomide disaster and other medical scandals in which new drugs were given to human subjects without their informed consent, Senator Javits of New York attached a "patient consent" amendment to the Drug Amendments Act of 1962, also known as the Kefauver–Harris Act. The act, on which Senator Kefauver had been holding hearings since 1959, was passed as a result of the horror over the thalidomide disaster, in which many children were born with undeveloped limbs because their mothers had taken thalidomide during the first trimester of pregnancy. Javits's amendment, like the rest of the act, pertained only to drug experiments and accordingly assigned responsibility for its enforcement to the Food and Drug Administration. The F.D.A., though it had probably had statutory authority to act otherwise since 1938, had always been permissive about regulation of the use of human subjects, reflecting the generally passive and conservative views on informed consent of the medical research community at that time. (For further evidence on these views, see Welt, 1961.) In his speech in the Senate offering his amendment on patient consent, Senator Javits gave further evidence of this passivity by producing a legal research memorandum from the Library of Congress showing that not a single state had any statute covering the use of experimental drugs or requiring physicians to inform their patients that they were using experimental drugs. At that time, it was common practice for pharmaceutical companies to distribute their experimental drugs among ordinary physicians for clinical testing.

The F.D.A. was slow to take action on the Javits amendment; but in 1966, under a new commissioner, it finally issued a set of detailed regulations for informed consent. The interesting fact about these regulations is that they did not come from recent medical malpractice suits in common law. Indeed, they scarcely could have, since there had been so little working out of such regulations in those suits. Instead, the F.D.A. took its regulations from the Nuremberg Code and the Helsinki Declaration. Here is a clear case of a nongovernmental code expressing a new set of values that influenced the administrative fulfilment of a statutory law. This is what the F.D.A.'s 1966 regulation, "Consent for Use of Investigational New Drugs on Humans: Statement of Policy," had to say about informed consent:

> "Consent" or "informed consent" means that the person involved has legal capacity to give consent, is so situated as to be able to exercise free power of choice, and is provided with a fair explanation of all material information concerning the administration of the investigational drug, or his possible use as a control, as to enable him to make an understanding decision as to his willingness to receive said investigational drug. This latter element requires that before the acceptance of an affirmative decision by such person the investigator should make known to him the nature, duration, and purpose of the administration of said investigational drug; the method and means by which it is to be administered; all inconveniences and hazards reasonably to be expected, including the fact, where applicable, that the person may be used as a control; the existence of alternative forms of therapy, if any; and the effects upon his health or person that may possibly come from the administration of the investigational drug. Said patient's consent shall be obtained in writing by the investigator.

The statement allowed some exceptions where a drug was being administered therapeutically, but none at all for non-therapeutic research. The exceptions in therapeutic use were, in effect, the therapeutic privilege, where the doctor considers that informing the patient may be contrary to the patient's best interests. The F.D.A. regulations on informed consent were a big step forward in specifying the principle of informed consent. They were, said Curran, "a considerable accomplishment from the legal viewpoint" (1969, p. 590).

The other major administrative specification of the informed consent principle came from the National Institutes of Health and its parent organization, the Department of Health, Education, and Welfare. In this case, administrative action resulted not from the express requirements of statutory law but from self-generated initiatives from the institutes' medical research and legal staffs that research subjects, both intramurally and extramurally, be given the right of informed consent. After many internal and informal actions, the institutes published their own policy statement on human research in 1966, a statement under continual revision ever since. The original 1966 statement assigned responsibility for ethical review of human research to local peer review committees in each institution receiving funds from the National Institutes of Health. So far as informed consent was concerned, this statement specified only that local review should consider "the appropriateness of the methods used to secure informed consent." Subsequent revisions of the statement have gone on to give detailed regulations for informed consent much like those of the Helsinki Declaration and the F.D.A. regulations. In 1974, Congress passed a new statute setting up the National Commission for the Protection of Human Subjects to make studies and give advice to the secretary of Health, Education, and Welfare, on all matters regarding the ethics of biomedical and behavioral research. One of the prime charges to the commission in its statute of enactment was to investigate and improve the whole area of informed consent. Several activities of the commission have been directed toward this end.

It should be noticed that these statutory and administrative legal definitions of the principle and rules of informed consent have moved away from the analogy to tort law, that is, the law of personal liability and battery, toward a law of regulation, that is, as Curran puts it, a law "seeking to prevent harm from being done to research subjects, rather than to redress harm already done" (1969, p. 550). Curran feels that peer review committees, in considering instances of rules of informed consent, can learn a great deal from the procedures and practices of administrative law concerning regulatory and licensing adjudication.

Despite this great progress in statutory and administrative

law, the courts have not entirely abandoned the search for better standards of informed consent in cases where experimentation and therapy overlap. In 1969, Dr. Denton A. Cooley implanted the first totally mechanical heart into the chest of a patient named Haskell Karp. This heart kept the patient alive for about sixty-four hours, when a human heart transplant was performed. Mr. Karp died a day and a half later. The patient's wife brought suit against Cooley for gross negligence and lack of informed consent. At the first trial, in the Federal District Court in Texas, the judge directed a verdict for the physician defendant. The case was appealed to the Federal Court of Appeals, where a three-judge bench unanimously held for the defendant. In this important decision, the court followed the majority rule that gives great weight to medical judgment but also laid heavy emphasis on the fact that Cooley had obtained from Mrs. Karp what Curran, in a review of this case, calls "a well drafted consent form that was specifically designed for the case at hand" (1974, pp. 1015–1016). This court obviously did not feel, as some doctors and lawyers have argued, that consent forms are "worthless." The court was approving of the fact that the consent form was specifically prepared for Mr. Karp's case and that it gave the details of the nature of the procedure to be performed on him, its purposes, and the risks and inconveniences reasonably to be expected. Thus not only statutory law and administrative regulations have been making progress with informed consent; so too have the courts trying common law cases. Best of all, the several types of law seem to be interacting creatively with one another.

CHANGES AND PROPOSED CHANGES

The present legal scene for informed consent contains much movement, some of it toward definitely established change, the rest in flux where it is hard to discern any permanent direction. Definite change has occurred in that the law has now moved, both in statute and in court decisions, toward giving more weight to the principle of informed consent than it formerly did. We have seen that this change has occurred indirectly, in the case of medical therapy, through the extension of

the tort principle of battery to require better procedures for obtaining informed consent from patients. The change has occurred directly, in the case of medical research, through statutory and administrative enactments that borrow from various
nongovernmental codes the principles and rules that establish
the importance and independence of informed consent. While
the law of informed consent has proceeded most rapidly in the
United States, where the volume of experimental research is
greatest, it has also been changing in other industrial countries.
In Italy, for example, as a result of charges of "human guinea pig
experiments," legislation has been passed in Liguria, the region
(including Genoa) where the alleged evils occurred, requiring
informed consent for all "new therapy." (See account in *Medical
Tribune,* June 21, 1972.)

Although we can note that there has been definite change in
the importance legally given to the principle of informed consent, we can only speak of flux and uncertain movement with
regard to the standards courts hold to prove malfeasance in this
area. A few have moved away from the majority standard, which
rests on expert testimony, toward a minority rule, which rests on
a layman's definitions of the reasonable man. In 1972 alone, five
courts asserted the minority rule in cases that came before
them.

One of the most important of these was *Canterbury* v. *Spence,*
in which the United States Court of Appeals in the District of
Columbia circuit dispensed with the expert witness requirement. In this case the judge held, "Many of the issues particu-
larly involved in nondisclosure cases do not reside peculiarly
within the medical domain. Lay witness testimony can compe-
tently establish a physician's failure to disclose particular risk
information, the patient's lack of knowledge of the risk, and the
adverse consequences following treatment. Experts are unnecessary to a showing of the materiality of risk to a patient's
decision on treatment or to the reasonably expected failure of
risk disclosure on the decision" (cited in Rubsamen, 1973, p.
27). Following *Canterbury,* a decision from which it quoted lib-
erally in its own decision, the Supreme Court of California in
Cobbs v. *Grant* also discarded the standard of the expert medical community. Although these two courts are influential in the
legal community, it is hard to know either if the new standard
they proclaimed will be followed in other courts or how soon.

One legal commentator predicts the likelihood that the minority rule will become the majority rule: "What do these decisions forecast for the rest of the country?" Rubsamen has asked. "I feel it is likely that the element of 'consumerism' implicit in them will prove to be influential for the high courts in other states. In only a few years, therefore, the traditional law on informed consent may be history in many, if not most states" (1973, p. 29). This prediction has not yet been realized. We have flux still rather than established change. Courts in Pennsylvania, Washington, and Rhode Island have followed California and Washington, D.C.; but the majority have not. (See Simonaitis, 1972, 1973.) As we have seen earlier, Professor Jay Katz is not surprised by this failure of the majority to go along.

> Though judges have felt morally bound to announce that patients ought to be enabled to guide their medical fate, they considered this position unsatisfactory in application and subjected it to extensive modifications. That such modifications significantly tampered with the basic posit of patients' self-determination and that altogether judicial commitment to individual decision making was not very firm, were never clearly admitted. Judicial concern about patients' capacity to make medical decisions and about the detrimental impact of disclosure on patients proved to be more influential than self-determination in shaping the informed consent doctrine, even though the validity of these concerns rests more on conjecture than fact (1977, p. 141).

Whether the principle of informed consent is fully established or still in flux, it is agreed by all legal commentators that the principles and rules are too general and amorphous for easy and comfortable application either in administrative decisions or in the courts or by individual physicians. Our legal commentators recommend that further specificity be given to these rules through continuous court adjudication and administrative action. In this way, legal generalities move toward more concrete application—through specific decisions and cases. Some commentators, however, have recommended that the courts take a big step forward by borrowing the more specific rules about disclosure already developed in nongovernmental codes and the government statutes built on them (Note, 1973). All the different forms of the law would then be abreast of one another, with all the remaining amorphousness and ambiguity to be reduced by further (and preferably collaborative) actions and decisions taken by each of them. One caution seems in order for the longer run—that specificity in rules governing informed consent should not go so far as to abolish professional judgment altogether, as exercised by the individual physician either alone or in consultation with an effective peer review group. The present short-run need is clearly greater specificity of the rules of informed consent; but in the longer run, the limits set by other requirements of the doctor–patient relationship should be kept in view.

Legal commentators, who tend to view doctor–patient interaction as primarily a one-on-one relationship, a matter of effective communication between the two, have recommended a number of other specific changes in informed consent procedures that follow from their view of this relationship. For example, it has been recommended that "the duty to obtain consent should fall on the physician primarily in charge of administering the treatment, since he is typically the only doctor to speak to the patient and because he coordinates all phases of the treatment" (Note, 1973). It is also recommended that the physician should obtain consent before beginning treatment, and finally, that the responsible physician make disclosure through a mixture of oral and written methods. He should start with oral disclosure, carefully constructing his communication to suit the understanding and needs of the individual patient; but he should then put the substance of what he discloses into a written document which the patient signs, not only as a confirmation of what he has understood but as a form of protection for the physician. We have seen in the Karp suit against Dr. Cooley that the courts placed great emphasis on a written, individually constructed consent form in holding for the defendant. The form of consent, however, is less important then the substance. In the last analysis, whether consent is obtained orally, in written form, or by some mixture of these two, a court will look for evidence of adequate disclosure and valid consent. If these are not present, a signed form is not enough. As James Vaccarino has stressed, "conversation" and "mutuality" are the essences of informed consent; whether oral or written, an informed consent must contain these two essential features (1978, p. 455).

It is probable, of course, that there is considerably limited variability in the presenting situations doctors and experimenters face in dealing with patients and subjects. It would be useful if groups of doctors, their professional associations, or hospitals were to prepare an adequate number of standard consent statements for these situations. An individual doctor might modify these statements slightly, but he would not have to draw each one up in its entirety in each case. Such a recommendation reaches beyond the physician–patient pair to the larger social system in which they are involved. All these recommendations are intended to increase the physician's legal security by specifying the scope and substance of his legal duty.

THE LAW'S LIMITS

Having now seen so clearly the influence of the law in advancing the principle of informed consent, we may close our discussion by noting the law's limits as a social control mechanism. (See Burt, 1977.) The law has not done and cannot do its work in this area all by itself. It is interdependent with changes in value and norm systems, with communications patterns, with educational structures, and with a whole variety of informal professional social control mechanisms. Because it is only one part of the larger social system, the law is more effective when other parts of the social system are working in the same direction. As one legal scholar has put it: "Finally, then, the law as a system of control is not in any realistic, creative sense distinct from private and semipublic centers and organs of control. . . . There is, or should be a fusion, one might even say a fruitful *con-fusion,* of legal and extralegal norms and of legal and extralegal mechanisms" (Jaffe, 1969, p. 414). Although it is important never to underestimate what Professor Grad has called "the real bite of the law," still other social control mechanisms are also important. We shall discuss this matter further in later chapters.

4

Authority, Power, and Informed Consent

One common complaint against the modern doctor is that he is authoritarian and in consequence does not satisfactorily inform his patients about either their therapy or their use as research subjects. Is this complaint justified? What are the authority relations between doctor and patient, and how do they affect the exchange of necessary information? These are important questions; and in this chapter, we shall concentrate on the matter of authority relations, reserving for the next most of the evidence on how communication actually proceeds. The type of authority prevailing in a social relationship is an important determinant of its effectiveness in achieving the goals of the participants. Their satisfaction in and with the relationship is vitally affected by their feelings about the authority or power they exercise over one another. In a discussion prepared for the National Commission for the Protection of Human Subjects on "the myriad of ethical issues" arising in "the delivery of health care," David Mechanic, one of our leading medical sociologists, says:

The crux of the issue, I believe, is the inequality between provider and patient and the extent to which these inequalities are growing with changes in the organization and provision of health care. Mechanisms are necessary, therefore, that contribute to narrowing these inequalities and that provide effective feedback to administrators and other professionals as to the problems and experiences of patients. In short, it is essential to develop countervailing influence by patients in the care process (1978, p. 31).

Among the mechanisms Mechanic suggests are grievance procedures and ombudsmen. We shall discuss such suggestions more fully in Chapter 6 in connection with our account of hospital review committees as social control mechanisms.

To answer our questions, we need to look briefly at the nature and uses of authority and power in social systems and social relationships in general. Then we need to consider how this general analysis applies specifically in medical systems and relationships. What kind of authority is required to make these systems and relationships effective and satisfactory to the participants, and what kind of authority actually prevails? We shall see that social analysts differ about both questions. Finally, we need to consider all the evidence we can find about what does in fact occur—what kind of authority is exercised between doctors and patients. Because we shall find that the evidence is not so good as it could be, the answers to our questions will necessarily be tentative. But because authority and power affect all other aspects of social relationships—not least of all those in the medical realm—we need to answer our questions as best we can. Tentative answers may also suggest new ways of asking the questions and new kinds of evidence needed to give better answers.

AUTHORITY AND POWER IN SOCIAL SYSTEMS AND RELATIONSHIPS

For our brief definitional analysis of authority and power in social systems and social relationships, we start with the obvious but essential fact that there is a need to establish goals and to choose means for achieving them in all social systems and relationships. There usually are several alternatives. Although we sometimes think this is true only of large and complex social systems—political states and other complex forms of social organization—it is equally true for the smallest social systems such as nuclear families or friendships. It is likewise true not only for medical systems in the most comprehensive sense—that is, at the national level—but also for hospitals and for doctors and patients meeting one another in the simpler relationships of solo practice.

While there is always a certain amount of openness, of negotiation and renegotiation, in defining and choosing goals and means in social systems, there is also a certain structured quality to this endless process. The capacity to define and choose is assigned to certain roles, and thus there emerges and exists a certain structured capacity for getting things done. Because this capacity is so important to all members of the social system, their values and interests are deeply involved in it. Strong moral sentiments both on the part of those assigned the capacity to choose goals and means and on the part of those affected by these choices focus on the roles assigned the responsibility for decision. Because of this moral dimension, we speak of "authority" or "legitimacy" when there is a moral consensus among all parties to a social relationship or all members of a social system that a certain role and its occupant rightfully perform the task of choosing goals and means. Of course, *moral consensus* is usefully thought of as a matter of degree, not as an absolute that either does or does not exist—authority and legitimacy are seldom complete. There may always be some dissensus, some complaints, some resentment over the goals and means chosen by "the authorities" to guide the system. If we may say that *authority* exists when the degree of moral consensus is relatively high, then we may define *power* as the opposite condition, one that exists when the degree of moral consensus is low, when a considerable number of participants in the system disapprove of the goal or means chosen by their leaders. *Power,* in this sense, is a frequent ingredient of social systems and relationships. All of us tolerate a certain amount of it, contenting ourselves with expressing complaints or feeling resentment; but sometimes we try to do something about it, either by replacing a particular powerful leader with a more authoritative one or by altering the leadership role itself because we become convinced that the role rather than its occupant is causing our trouble.

Because authority and power are so important, we have a large and somewhat confusing vocabulary for referring to them. For example, in speaking of very powerful political systems, systems in which there is much moral disagreement between the public and the leaders, we often us the term *authoritarian*. The same term has been used, however, in a form of accepted exaggeration, for much milder degrees of power. It is probably in this milder mode that the term has been applied to doctors. We turn now to exploring the types of authority and power said to be needed and to prevail in medical therapy and research relationships.

AUTHORITY AND POWER PATTERNS IN MEDICAL RELATIONSHIPS

Because of the great importance of authority and power in medical systems and relationships, they have inevitably become central foci of discussion in medical sociology. Unfortunately, this discussion has been much more theoretical than empirical. Although those who offer various theoretical analyses claim that they are empirically valid, they support these claims more by selective personal impressions and experience and occasional research than by systematic, cumulative evidence. Two different analytic models have come to be predominant: one we may call *the collegiality model,* the other *the dominance model*. The former is offered as a model of what would prevail in medical relationships if they were to achieve the greatest effectiveness and satisfaction for all participants. It may be thought of as a model of the ideal medical relationship, though there is no question that it occasionally occurs in actual practice and could occur more frequently if a variety of changes were made in medical relationships. The dominance model, on the other hand, is offered as an account of the actual state of authority relationships in medical systems, given the conditions in which it presently operates. Those conditions are not immutable, but they would have to be changed if present medical dominance patterns were to be transformed into collegiality patterns.

The creator of the collegiality model is Talcott Parsons, whose interest in the nature of medical systems and relationships goes back at least forty years. (See especially, Parsons, 1939; 1951, Chap. 10; 1969.) Parsons's model is concerned primarily with the patient or subject on the one side and the physician, physician team, or researcher on the other. He gives much less emphasis than does Freidson, the creator of the dominance model, to the relationships of the patient or subject to paramedical personnel in the hospital or to the relationships among doctors themselves. For Parsons, "patients are conceived as 'cooperating' with their physicians or therapeutic 'teams' in a common enterprise within the framework of solidarity" (1969, p. 334). This emphasis on cooperation in a common enterprise characterized by solidarity—by presumed consensus on goals and means and consequent legitimacy—is at the heart of Parsons's assertion that collegial, or a relatively equal, distribution of authority is the appropriate mode for medical relationships. If the medical relationship is, as Parsons sees it, an "associational collectivity" with full rights on both sides to enter or to withdraw from the collectivity, then the collegial type of authority will occur in medical relationships as it tends to in all associational collectivities. Parsons holds that "interaction with respect to professional function is not nearly so one-sided as it is often held to be. Clients are not, in general, simply passive recipients of service; they are contributors to the common output of the cooperative system" (1969, p. 340). In support of this empirical generalization, Parsons refers to the study by Fox in which she describes the collaboration between researchers and subjects on a medical ward where highly innovative and experimental medication and surgery were being tried out (Fox, 1959). This case, however, seems to be almost unique, a result both of the strong feelings of uncertainty and indecision the researchers felt in the situation and of the personal and prolonged (even intimate) contact between the physicians and their patient-subjects. (On the special and unusual character of the situation described by Fox, see Lally and Barber, 1974). In an analysis of a similar situation of novelty and uncertainty, that of genetic counseling by pediatricians, Sorenson has pointed to a similar constraint on the usual authoritativeness of the physicians (1974). These special conditions do not obtain in most medical therapy and research, which is routine and presents relatively little uncertainty. Indeed, as we shall see when we examine the great authoritativeness of surgeons trying out novel and dangerous cardiac surgery, physicians do not always move toward collegiality, even in situations of uncertainty and novelty.

Parsons defines collegiality not as the existence of complete equality between physician and patient but as a *relative* reduction in the differences of authority assigned to these two roles. He insists that there must be some structured difference of authority because of what he calls "the competence gap." This gap must exist because the physician is in command of "technical" knowledge acquired through long training and experience, which the patient or subject cannot have. Parsons notes that "the ultimate responsibility for standards both of competence and of integrity must rest with the professional complex itself," and that physicians must therefore have the greater authority that goes with this ultimate responsibility (1969, p. 329). In the case of the physician, this technical knowledge is presumably knowledge about biological structure and function. It should be pointed out immediately that other kinds of knowledge are involved in medical relationships and that physicians do not necessarily have any special technical competence in these other kinds of knowledge. For example, medical relationships always have social and moral dimensions; and in these the patient may feel that his competence is as great as that of his physician. Claims by laymen that they have as much moral knowledge as physicians about "life" and "death" in cases of abortion and terminal illness are indicative of moral problems of this kind. (See Crane, 1975, for a study of physicians' unawareness of the moral stands they are taking in these matters.) Sorenson, in his discussion of new procedures for genetic counseling by physicians, has described a case where physicians themselves are aware that there may be no moral "competence gap" between them and their patients (1974).

We have heard many complaints against the "medicalization" of society (Illich, 1976; Fox, 1976). These complaints express in its most generalized form the protest against medicine's assumption of a special competence in the social and moral aspects and consequences of medical relationships. They reject the notion that there is a "competence gap" in these matters. As one complainant against the "medicalization" of behavior and society has put it:

I must confess that given the road down which so much expertise has taken us, I am willing to live with some of the frustrations and even mistakes that will follow when the authority for many decisions becomes shared with those whose lives and activities are involved. For I am convinced that patients have so [sic] much to teach to their doctors as do students their professors and children their parents (Zola, 1972, p. 502).

Parsons is not the only one to describe the collegiality model. Professor Paul Freund, an expert on Constitutional law who has been much interested in medical ethics, has outlined the characteristics of what he calls "the voluntary community," which is "marked by a measure of reciprocity of duties and powers," where the "duty to cooperate persists until legitimately ended," where the patient has a "share in the governance of the community," and where he has "a final veto . . . so far as his part is concerned" (1969, pp. 318 ff.). Freund is not content, however, to leave such collegiality to the patient and physician alone. He thinks that the collegial model "calls for structural safeguards," such as peer review or a special medical advisor to protect the patient's interests. The suggestion of structural safeguards, of course, implies either that the collegial model is not one of near equality or (which is more likely) that it easily changes into a dominance model.

Finally, Margaret Mead has asserted that Parsons's collegial model "presents as an ideal what has long been anthropological field practice" (1969, p. 361). In this area, she feels that researchers and subjects are engaged in a "cooperative enterprise" in which subjects are not "guinea pigs"—experimental animals who symbolize the essence of powerlessness—but active participants, paid (when they are paid) "as compensation for the time that would otherwise be spent in hunting, fishing, or gardening" (1969, p. 362). Mead offers no evidence for this empirical generalization.

Eliot Freidson is the creator of what we have called the dominance model, which offers a paradigm of the authority structure in the medical system at least implicitly in direct opposition to Parsons's collegiality model. Taken explicitly, such paradigmatic differences provide one of the useful ways in which social science can test and advance our understanding, in this case of authority and power in the medical system and its consequences for information processes and informed consent.

Unlike Parsons, who tends to concentrate his analysis on the immediate relationship of physician and patient, Freidson is concerned with the health system as a whole in its most inclusive and comprehensive form. Thus he is much more concerned than Parsons about all the different social relationships that occur in the medical world, not only those between patient and doctor but those between doctors and other professions and paraprofessions, between doctors and doctors, and between doctors and medical administrators. He is also concerned about the relations between the organized medical profession and other public organizations and the government itself.

For Freidson, the central empirical fact that needs explanation is the dominance of the medical profession over all other groups and individuals in the health system. In his book, *Professional Dominance*, he asserts at the outset that "health services are organized around professional authority, and their basic structure is constituted by the dominace of a single profession over a variety of other, subordinate occupations. I shall argue that professional dominance is the analytical key to the present inadequacy of the health services" (1970, p. xi). Or again, "many of the rigid, mechanical, and authoritarian attributes, and much of the inadequate coordination said to characterize the health services, may stem more from their professional organization than from their bureaucratic characteristics" (1970, p. 132).

On what is this dominance based? Freidson thinks that the medical profession has used what Parsons calls "the competence gap" to subordinate its patients and other groups in the medical system unnecessarily and unfairly. Although Freidson acknowledges that there may be some technical competence gap with respect to biological knowledge, he does not accept any gap so far as the moral aspects of medical relationships are concerned. The subordination of patients and others to doctors "is based on the assumption that a professional has such special esoteric knowledge and humanitarian intent that he and he alone should be allowed to decide what is good for the layman" (1970, p. 132). Freidson does not agree that the physician's technical and scientific knowledge or his moral excellence is such that it requires him to dominate his patients, assistants, and associates as he presently does. For Freidson, the medical system is not so much a cooperative enterprise, as is claimed in the collegial model, as a hierarchical organization with doctors at the apex. As one alienated doctor put it in a letter to the editor of the *New England Journal of Medicine,* "Two words in common medical usage that indicate the current attitude of physicians toward their patients are 'order' and 'compliance.' The doctor's order requires the patient to take a medicine or to perform some task. Compliance is the term used to indicate whether or not the patient followed the order." Obviously preferring the collegiality model to the dominance model, the letter writer goes on, "When physicians' attitudes toward their patients change enough to replace the term doctor's 'order' with health 'contract' a major obstacle to execution of that contract will be gone" (Plaut, 1975, p. 438).

The medical profession maintains its dominance, Freidson's analysis continues, because it is too autonomous; it evaluates and controls others but is itself neither subject to the judgment of others nor effectively self-regulating. With the exception of dentistry, which has escaped from the dominance of medicine by removing itself on the whole from the hospital, where the medical profession rules, "the only occupation that is truly autonomous is medicine itself. It has the authority to direct and evaluate the work of others without in turn being subject to formal direction and evaluation by them" (1970, p.136.). The medical profession has established a hierarchy of expertise as dominant over those it controls as the hierarchies of office that prevail in bureaucracies.

One obvious consequence of the dominance structure is poor communication and lack of informed consent for patients, a condition of medical treatment that many patients resent. Freidson describes this phenomenon vividly:

> The extent to which the staff withholds information from the patient and avoids communicative interaction with him has been a common criticism of the operation of such medical organizations as hospitals. The complaint is that no one tells the client what is going to be done to him, why, and when. And after he has been treated no one tells him why he feels the way he does, what can be expected subsequently, and whether or not he will live or die. The charge is that so little information is provided him that the patient cannot evaluate why he is being treated in a certain manner. Experience is mysteriously meaningless when it includes long waits for something unknown to happen or for something that does not happen, being awakened for an apparently trivial reason, being examined by taciturn strangers who enter the

room, unintroduced, perceiving lapses in such routines as medication and feeding without knowing whether error or intent is at issue (1970, p.139).

Freidson does not think that the essential reason for such poor communication lies in the faults of bureaucratic structure. After all, a bureaucracy could work out standardized, routine ways of getting information to patients. For example, they could create "brochures explaining and justifying hospital routines, describing the experience of 'typical' cholycystectomies, mastectomies, or heart patients from the first day through convalescence, and including answers to 'commonly asked questions' " (1970, p. 139). He thinks the essential reason stems from professional dominance. Doctors instruct nurses and other hospital workers to tell the patients nothing

By and large, without medical authorization, paramedical workers are not supposed to communicate anything of significance to the patient about what his illness is, how it will be treated, and what the chances are for improvement. The physician himself is inclined to be rather jealous of the prerogative and is not inclined to authorize other workers to communicate information to the patient. Consequently, the paraprofessional worker who is asked for information by a patient is inclined to pass the buck like any bureaucrat. "You'll have to ask your doctor," the patient is told (1970, p. 140).

Nor, acting from the stance of professional dominance, does the doctor feel he himself needs to communicate well and fully with patient or subject. In part, this may result from uncertainty about the patient's diagnosis or prognosis, although the amount of uncertainty is easy to exaggerate; and in part, from a heavy schedule, although in that case, he could do more to delegate his authority. But mostly, thinks Freidson, it results from the physician's assumption of the necessary passivity and subordination of the patient. The doctor characteristically assumes that the patient is too ignorant to understand the information he gets or too upset to use the information rationally and responsibly. The doctor assumes that giving the patient good information will only create an additional management problem for himself.

Thus, the patient should not be treated like an adult, but rather like a child, given reassurance but not information. To do otherwise would only lead to the patient being upset and making unnecessary trouble for the staff. Characteristically, the professional does not view the client as an adult, responsible person (1970, p. 141).

Because of this assumption of the patient's incompetence and irresponsibility, Freidson holds, medical professionals insist so strongly that patients and subjects must have "faith" and "trust" in them. If a patient does not have sufficient faith, they say, then he should change doctors, to one in whom he has sufficient faith. But such faith or trust is based not on exchange of information and demonstration of competence but on an unreasoning, unquestioning faith in the doctor's self-ascribed competence and dominance. "Insistence on faith constitutes insistence that the client give up his role as an independent adult" (1970, p. 141). Faith and trust can be built either upon persuasion through information or upon authoritarian fiat. Freidson feels that too much of the present medical call for faith is based on fiat.

Finally, Freidson feels that doctors, operating within the professional dominance model, develop an "imperialistic ideology" that extends their power unwarrantedly even beyond the immediate problems of medical therapy and research. For example, they exert "a special and biased influence on planning and financing" health services in general. It is clear that Freidson thinks that the power structures and "politics" of the immediate health situation are the basis on which the power structures and politics of the profession in the larger society rest. They both come from the same professional dominance patterns, from the same assumptions about self and patients.

From both the collegial and the dominance models, it is clear that one of their central points of focus lies in what they assume about the patient's behavior and what they assert is the doctor's assumption about the patient's behavior. The collegial model treats the patient as in principle active and asserts that the physician makes the same behavioral assumption. The dominance model asserts that the physician makes assumptions about the patient's passivity and dependence but implies that this assumption is not necessarily correct, or at least need not be correct. We need to test these assumptions, implied or expressed, about patients' behavior. Are patients active and autonomous decisionmakers who can participate effectively in more nearly equal, collegial relationships? Or are they necessarily passive and dependent, with a need to be protected, to be reassured rather than informed, and to be told what to do for their own good, which they find hard to know? Better still, we need to be more specific in our inquiries into patient behavior. What do they have the capacity to understand and decide? What kinds of patients in what kinds of situations have what kind of capacity for knowledge and cooperative decision making? Certainly the blanket assumption of incapacity has not and will not lead to systematic investigations in medicine to find answers to these questions. They are too seldom taken as questions. Nor is there much of an effort on the part of physicians or others to create active, independent patients. The assumption of incapacity may be a self-fulfilling prophecy.

SOME EVIDENCE ON AUTHORITY AND POWER PATTERNS

We have now looked at two models—the collegial and the dominance—offered as paradigmatic descriptions of the authority relations that prevail in medical relationships and systems. Which seems to be more in accord with the empirical realities? The evidence to answer this question definitively is not yet at hand: we do not have enough specific and carefully collected data for a satisfactory answer. It is nevertheless our impression that the weight of the evidence leans more toward the dominance model. It is clear, however, that the collegiality model is realized in some special situations and could be more widely realized if a number of changes were made in the present medical system. We shall consider some of these changes at the end of this chapter and throughout the rest of the book. Changes in authority patterns depend on a variety of changes in other parts of the medical system. Let us now consider our sparse and scattered evidence.

The Physician and the General Public

For all the allegations of medical authoritarianism made by patients among the general public, we face the rather startling fact that when we look for systematic and solid evidence to support the charge, we do not find it. (For systematic survey data on the fact that the charge is often made and that attitudes challenging physician authority do exist, see Haug and Lavin, 1978.) As we shall see in Chapter 5, there is ample direct evidence that physicians do not communicate well with patients and subjects; this is sometimes attributed to authoritarianism, but it may as well be due to other causes. We do not have direct evidence of physician authoritarianism; nobody has actually observed doctor–patient *interaction* on a systematic and representative basis with this problem in view, nor has anyone made a systematic study of the *attitudes* of patients or physicians on the matter of authority. Instead of observational or attitudinal survey studies, what we have is a kind of modern "murmuring of the masses," widespread informal complaints by and among patients, who apparently seldom express their anger and resentment directly to their physicians. Instead, they "vote with their feet" by leaving one doctor for another, and then perhaps another, and then by accepting a system and pattern of authority that is all too uniform but about which they come to feel they can do nothing but accept and silently resent. This observation does not imply that all patients would like to be treated more equally and given more information with which to share in medical decision making. Such a situation is unlikely; the present system is too well established for that. But it is clear that all we know about is a "murmuring of the masses." We do not know what proportion of the general public is so murmuring or how strongly it feels its antiauthoritarian resentments. We know from public opinion polls that on balance medicine is widely respected in our society; but this finding is not inconsistent with the possibility that there is considerable ambivalence, a considerable admixture of resentment on the matter of authority with gratitude for the efficacy of medical treatment. Satisfaction with medical relationships is no more an all-or-nothing matter than is satisfaction with other types of social relationships. As guidance for action and possible reform in this area, we need direct, objective, systematic, representative studies, probably both observational and attitudinal surveys of the authority dimension of doctor–patient relationships.

Although we have no systematic evidence on the authority behavior or attitudes of doctors and patients and although the complaints of patients are seldom made public and permanent in published form, we do have some statements by physicians that provide one kind of evidence about their views on authority. It appears that some of these views would easily result in what many patients might think of as authoritarian behavior. An example is provided in the book by Dr. Brian Bird, *Talking with Patients,* now in its second edition (1973). Dr. Bird favors more talking by physicians to patients and more listening by them as patients talk. He has useful pointers on common faults in the ways doctor talk with their patients and useful guides toward the improvement of medical conversations. All this looks like a recommendation for more equality and patient participation in therapeutic and research encounters. Dr. Bird's extended and explicit views on the transcendent authority of the physician, however, are not at all egalitarian. Because his views encapsulate an attitude toward authority that many physicians may share, because they express an attitude that many patients may resent, and because of their publication in a book that his colleagues and medical students may consult as authoritative, it is worth reporting these views at considerable length:

> One little understood thing that distinguishes being a doctor from not being one is the position a doctor assumes relative to people who come to him for help. The doctor's way of responding to requests for help is his special thing; it is a quality that transcends knowledge, a quality that demands a unique sense of responsibility for human life, a responsibility built on an almost arrogant kind of confidence in himself, a quality that has evolved from the age-old tradition of patient care.

> Above everything else, "becoming a doctor" requires the wearing of his title of "Doctor" firmly and well. In order to perform the things he has learned in school, he must take this further step, must accept within himself the seemingly arrogant idea to do the unusual, peculiar things "being a doctor" demands of him. Officially, of course, this authority is established by various documents: his medical degree, his hospital diploma, his specialty certificate, and his license to practice. But these documents do not really attest to his "being a doctor." This final authority must come from him: he must have the nerve, confidence, the gall, or whatever it takes, to grant it unto himself (1973, pp. 14–15).

Notice that Dr. Bird mentions that this pattern of transcendent authority is an "age-old tradition of patient care." And notice the extreme individualism of his view of authority. It is not something worked out in interaction with patients, something based on performance and persuasion, but rather something "arrogantly" self-assigned. We continue with Dr. Bird's views:

> The assumption of this unique personal authority is needed, it seems, to make sure that doctors, while doing their extraordinary work, are not handicapped by thinking of themselves as ordinary persons. Ordinary people do ordinary things. Only extraordinary people do extraordinary things.
>
> Taking this extra step, accepting this role, is not always possible. Some doctors cannot do it. They refuse to be set apart, refuse to see themselves as exceptions. Some may go part way but retain a lingering uneasiness at being called "Doctor," at being revered or regarded in a special way by their patients. . . . They do not see that the role is necessary for both doctor and patient.
>
> Some doctors not only cannot accept this role for themselves, but they cannot tolerate it in other doctors. They argue that patients should be treated as "equals," that the "consumer" should decide how he should be treated. While it is easy to support wholeheartedly the consumer's right to decide what he consumes, it is exceedingly dangerous, in my opinion, to do anything to destroy the doctor's sense of his special, even unique, attitude toward patient care, his sense of himself as an exception, someone who has been given the tremendous responsibility of doing to other human beings things that no one else is permitted normally to do. Only then, only when a doctor develops this benevolent but almost arrogant belief that it is right and proper for him to enter intimately into the life of his patients, will his medical skill, including talking with patients, reach a higher than ordinary level (1973, pp. 16–17).

Thus, Dr. Bird's ideal is one of a transcendent, self-imputed, benevolent authority for physicians in their dealings with patients and subjects. His ideal encourages more communication than now ordinarily occurs, but primarily on the doctor's terms. While all this seems to be an improvement over flat authoritarianism and no conversations with patients, it is probably still unsatisfactory to those patients who want more equality and participation in their medical relationships.

Medical Authority in the Hospital

Much of modern medical care takes place in hospitals, either on an in-patient basis or in the ambulatory out-patient services. Because a hospital is a public place with a great deal of division of labor, much of the behavior that occurs there is observable to people occupying a variety of roles in the medical system. We should expect to find more systematic evidence about authority patterns in hospitals than about those that prevail in more isolated doctors' offices. We do not, however, partly because doctors are in charge of hospitals. They determine who gains research access; and such access, as one study of hospital practices with regard to informed consent and risk–benefit ratios for human subjects of experiments reports, is obtained only under special conditions (Barber, 1973). As a result, what we have again is more the informal complaints and resentments of patients than systematic public evidence. (But see some good recent evidence in Carlton, 1978, pp. 114, 118, 161, and passim.) In a long and generalized discussion of "professional dominance" in the hospital, Freidson takes such dominance for granted but offers little in the way of evidence (1970, pp. 169–185). This dominance by physicians applies not only to patients, of course, but also *within* the medical hierarchy itself and *over* the assorted other groups of workers who staff modern hospitals, both those who call themselves professionals, such as nurses and social workers, and less skilled workers, such as technicians, orderlies, and cleaners. The "chief" of a medical service in a hospital has a degree of authority, based primarily on expertise rather than office, that is equal to that of any bureaucratic office holder.

One of the few aspects of the medical system where we can see the professional dominance of the physician most clearly is the relations between nurses and physicians in the hospital. (For reports on the ethical problems of nurses—only one of which centers on their subordination to physicians, though this is a key problem—see the following: Steinfels, 1977; Jameton, 1977; and Aroskar and Veatch, 1977.) Nurses, who formerly prided themselves on their complete subservience to physicians, indeed who used to define such subservience and obedience as one of their essential professional characteristics, have become restive and resentful in their relationships with physicians during the last twenty years. Nurses have joined such professional organizations as the American Nurses Association in increasing numbers; and these organizations have demanded (and often obtained) not only better pay and working conditions but some measure of greater equality and professional participation vis-a-vis the physician. Nurses now more often go on strike. For example, in 1974, four thousand nurses went on strike against forty-three hospitals in the Bay Area of northern California, demanding not only better pay and working-time conditions but "a greater voice in patient care in the hospitals" (*New York Times,* June 12, 1974). This strike coincided with the forty-ninth biennial convention of the American Nurses Association in San Francisco. It was a sign of the widespread agreement among nurses concerning their grievances against hospitals and physicians that the national convention passed a resolution in support of the local strikers' demands. Speaking at a press conference at the convention, one professor of nursing asserted that nurses everywhere in the country want a greater voice in hospital administration: "It is appropriate for physicians to say what constitutes effective medical care, and it is appropriate for nurses to determine what effective nursing care is" (*New York Times,* June 12, 1974). Apparently nurses do not feel they have adequate authority, even in their own sphere of competence, because of medical dominance in the hospital.

A survey of some ten thousand nurses across the country by *Nursing 77,* the largest nurses' journal in the United States, provides further evidence on the restiveness and resentment of nurses toward medical dominance (*New York Times,* January 9, 1977). Many respondents reported conflict with doctors over nursing care for patients, and they especially resented having to wait hours for a doctor to order what the nurse had already suggested should be done for a patient. Nurses feel that conditions for patients would improve if nurses had a voice at the top authority levels in hospitals and also in such other medical organizations concerned with quality control in hospitals as the national Joint Commission on Accreditation of Hospitals and the National Professional Standards Review Council. Obtaining representation on these two bodies has been made a first priority on the agenda of the American Nurses Association. However, Dr. John Porterfield, director of the joint commission, says that his organization is "loath to let more groups in," and Dr. William B. Munier, executive secretary of the National Professional Standards Review Council, which is funded by the Department of Health, Education, and Welfare, expresses sympathy for the A.N.A. but points out that "the law stipulates that only doctors can be admitted" (*New York Times,* January 9, 1977). Professional dominance is supported not only by informal custom and private organizations but also by public law. The law, of course, was made with the support of physicians.

The kind of subservience and excessive obedience on their part toward doctors that nurses hope to change has been clearly demonstrated in an experimental study of nurses' attitudes and behavior toward doctors' orders. (Hofling et al., 1966; it should be noted that under present regulations and review procedures for informed consent, this study might not have been allowed.) Hofling and his colleagues constructed an experiment in which nurses who were alone on their wards at the time were called by an unfamiliar voice, announcing itself to belong to a doctor and speaking in a tone of "courteous but self-confident firmness," and ordered to give "an obviously excessive dose of medicine" to a patient on the ward. Transmitting such orders by telephone was itself in violation of hospital policy, as the nurses knew. A member of the study team, a staff psychiatrist, was located where he could observe the nurse answering the phone, see whether she poured the medication, and stop her before she actually administered it. A half-hour later, after the study had been briefly explained to the nurse-subjects, a nurse member of the research group interviewed them further about the experience. This study included twenty-two nurses in medical, surgical, pediatric, and psychiatric wards in two different hospitals, one public and the other private.

The findings from the observed behavior and the subsequent interviews testify to the subservience of nurses to doctors' orders, even when they know there are many things wrong with them. First, of the twenty-two subjects, twenty-one proceeded toward giving the medication as ordered by the unfamiliar but authoritative doctor's voice. Second, these telephone calls were "invariably brief. Exclusive of time spent in looking for the medication, the calls averaged only two minutes in duration. Essentially no resistance to the order was expressed to the caller." Third, there was no delay after conclusion of the call in pouring the medication. Fourth, in their interviews, eleven of the subjects said they were aware during the experience that the dosage was excessive but acted anyway. Fifth, eighteen of the subjects indicated that they were aware of "the impropriety of nonemergency telephone orders" and added that it was not an uncommon impropriety. Sixth, none of the subjects became overtly hostile to the telephone caller, although in the interview sixteen of them said that they should have expressed greater resistance to this unwarranted order. Finally, in the interview, "fifteen of the subjects spontaneously recalled similar naturally occurring experiences. The remainder could recall such experiences when asked if they had occurred. A majority of the subjects referred to the displeasure of doctors on occasions when nursing resistance had been offered to instructions which had been considered improper."

The authors of this study suggest that so ingrained is the subservience of nurses to doctors, even when improper orders are given, that it exists "below the threshold of consciousness." This suggestion is supported by the fact that when the experimental situation was presented to twelve graduate nurses and twenty-one nursing students in questionnaire form, as a hypothetical possibility rather than in the real-life hospital stress situation, ten of twelve graduate nurses and all twenty-one student nurses said that they would not give the medication. The authors say that presumably,

> In a real-life situation corresponding to the experimental one, there would in theory, be two professional intelligences, the doctor's and the nurse's, working to ensure that a given procedure be undertaken in a manner beneficial to the patient or, at the very least, not detrimental to him. The experiment strongly suggests, however, that in the real-life situation one of these intelligences is, for all practical purposes, non-functioning (Hofling et al., 1966, p. 179).

Such is the reach and consequence of professional dominance on nurses' behavior. Such is the source, given their new awareness and aspiration, of nurses' organized striving for a greater share in the authority of medical care systems.

In a careful study, which they describe as a "partial replication" of the study by Hofling and colleagues just described, Rank and Jacobson report results "radically different" from those of the earlier study (1977). Their subject-nurses did not comply with the unknown doctor's orders to administer drug overdoses. They attribute this different behavior to two chief factors: first, in their study but not in the Hofling study, the nurses knew the prescribed drug very well and knew an overdose was being prescribed; second, they allowed their subjects to consult with nursing and other colleagues. Such peer discussion and support strengthened the subjects' tendencies to non-compliance. When we discuss obedience experiments by Professor Stanley Milgram, we shall see that peer consultation and support are important conditions for independent judgment in general. Rank and Jacobson feel that other lesser factors may have accounted in part for the different results: since the 1960s, doctors' judgments are increasingly questioned by both lay and nursing people; nurses increasingly differentiate between competent and incompetent physicians; nurses, like doctors, are worried about malpractice suits; and finally, these subjects, unlike those in the Hofling study, were volunteers of a kind and therefore may have behaved somewhat differently from the subjects in the earlier study.

Medical Authority and Innovative Surgery

Above all other kinds of medical specialists, the surgeon symbolizes and embodies authoritativeness and decisiveness in medical care. Nowhere is this authoritativeness more evident than in innovative surgery. For example, with the great increase in heart disease because of America's aging population, cardiac surgeons have moved decisively to "neovascularize and revascularize," as one distinguished cardiologist has put it, a growing number of those who suffer from heart disease (Spodick, 1971). The ill patient is confronted by an active, enthusiastic, authoritative person who recommends a remarkable new surgical procedure. Is the sick and frightened patient well informed when he gives consent? However much he is told, one essential fact is usually not disclosed: namely, that cardiac bypass surgery has never been subjected to controlled trials. It is only his surgeon's impression that this procedure is better than other treatments, medical and surgical, or no treatment at all; his surgeon does not have good scientific evidence for the superiority of his surgical innovations, the kind of evidence that comes from careful controlled trials of this procedure in comparison with others or with no treatment at all.

Such trials are coming to be standard procedure for nonsurgical medical innovations; they are legally required by the Food and Drug Administration for all new drugs. But surgeons persist in going their own decisive way, controlled to some extent by not too effective informal controls among themselves, but not requesting scrutiny or legitimation from outsiders, either medical specialists or laymen. A cardiologist critic of his surgical colleagues has provided some evidence of their failure to use controlled trials for their surgical innovations: "All issues for 1971 of 16 English-language specialty journals were reviewed, including 7 surgical, 4 cardiac, 3 internal medicine and 2 devoted to chest disease. All papers reporting the results of medical and surgical treatments for disease of the heart and the juxtacardiac great vessels were investigated for evidence that the trials were designed and executed in a controlled fashion" (Spodick, 1973, p. 579). His investigation was limited to those studies of alleged curative or ameliorative treatment for human beings for which there were alternative medical and /or surgical treatments. Of the seventy papers fulfilling the criteria for inclusion in the study, twenty-one were reports of medical therapy; and of these nine were controlled and seven were not. With the other five, the "question of a controlled design need not necessarily arise. By contrast, none of the 49 surgical reports involved a controlled study" (Spodick, 1973, p. 580).

On the whole, cardiac surgery is not unusual but typical of the great freedom from outside control and satisfactory disclosure of surgery in general. Spodick and other critics have spoken of the "schizoid behavior in the medical community" that requires controlled trials only of medical therapy and exempts the powerful surgeons from such controls. (Other informed commentators on this issue include Swazey, Klerman, and Neville, 1973; and in terms of a general discussion of the need for controlled trials, Chalmers, 1969; Shaw and Chalmers, 1970; and Chalmers, Block, and Lee, 1972.) To what is this special power of the surgeons using innovative therapy due? It has a number of sources, among which are such factors as the absence of outside funding and its consequent controls and the relative unobservability of innovative surgical procedures, especially in the early stages. Spodick has valiantly categorized the sources of surgeons' "barriers to acceptance of adequately controlled trials" into three different "human attributes," two different "statistical delusions," and six different "professional attributes" (1971, 1973). One of these professional attributes is especially relevant for our present concern about the ways in which professional authority turns into professional authoritarianism. Spodick labels one "professional attribute" as

"Olympianism." It seems to be not unlike professional dominance:

> The loftily self-sufficient doctor is convinced that he is a uniquely qualified judge of his own decisions, which therefore require little or no outside assistance. His efforts are ultimate efforts. This traditional godlike self-image is abetted by the adulation of the traditional dependent patient. In recent years olympianism may be weakening, but in many successful physicians and surgeons it blocks their receptivity for dangerous ideas, i.e., those which raise doubts (1971, p. 154).

Where doubts are not fully examined and made known to patients, only an authority based on ignorance or a power resented but accepted because there is no alternative can exist.

Medical Research and Psychological Obedience Experiments

To the great authority of the doctor in his traditional role as physician and healer has recently been added the great authority of the scientist. We often forget how recently what we now so easily and habitually call *scientific medicine* became widespread. It really goes back only forty or fifty years, burgeoning especially with the coming of the antibiotics in the 1940s. Indeed, the great prestige of science as a whole for the general public is not much older than that of scientific medicine. Today, scientific medicine is considered universal, however, and it has great prestige and power. This authority exists not only in the therapy context but also in the medical research situation. This transcendent authority makes submissive patients yield, however unwillingly, to doctors—as much because of their respect for and fear of science as because of their deference to doctors as healers.

We can see this transcendent authority and the consequent submissiveness of subjects in the research situation with especial clarity because of Professor Stanley Milgram's psychological obedience experiments (1974). Although psychological and medical research experiments are not identical, they share one essential characteristic: a claim in the name of the authority of science to the compliance and obedience of the subject. Milgram's psychological obedience experiments have something important to tell us about the authority that patients and subjects perceive in the medical research situation. Such perceptions evidently grant an undue power to the researcher in any situation defined as a scientific experiment.

The gist of Milgram's experiment and his findings is simple: subjects, who are not informed about the nature of the experiment in which they are asked to participate, are instructed to administer mild electric shocks to fake subjects who are seen only behind a glass screen and who pretend to be experiencing physical and emotional pain as a result of these shocks. The experimenter, who is really interested in seeing how far the real subjects will go, how obedient they will be to his scientific authority, keeps urging the subjects to administer ever more powerful shocks to the fake subjects. A majority of the subjects in a large number of experimental runs are highly obedient and give what they think are very powerful electric shocks to the fake subjects, shocks that make them writhe in a pretended agony that the real subject thinks is genuine. Although about one-third of the subjects in Milgram's experiments were not obedient, the majority were, probably because of their reluctance to disobey scientific "orders."

If people are willing to obey the scientist, even in such an emotionally and morally stressful situation as the one Milgram constructed for them, we can imagine how submissive they must be in the much less stressful situation that confronts them in most medical research situations. Most such situations are defined as routine, as part of that expectable (if not always necessary) stress that patients and subjects are accustomed to put up with in hospital situations. Such subjects are even less likely than Milgram's to challenge the authority of science, to ask to be informed, to refuse to obey. It is not surprising that they complain about medical authoritarianism when they are later informed that they have been in an experiment.

We should note another important similarity between Milgram's experiment and most medical research experiments. In both cases, the powerful experimenter typically confronts the lone and isolated potential subject, asking him on short notice and without opportunity to consult with friends and relatives, to decide whether or not to participate. On their own, without time for reflection, inquiry, or consultation with knowledgeable outsiders, individuals are more likely to be obedient than they would if they had more time to draw upon their own resources

or those of friends and helpful outsiders. The isolation of individuals from one another in the experimental situation is one
source of the great power of experimenters. There are two reasons for paying close attention to this isolation. First, when we
do, we are not likely to generalize too quickly, as Milgram unfortunately has, about the excessive submissiveness or obedience
of people in real-life situations. In real-life situations, people can
draw strength from their own careful consideration of the consequences of obedience and obtain the information and support they need to resist immoral or unwelcome orders, even
those from sources as authoritative as science and medicine.
Second, those concerned to make participation in experiments,
whether psychological or medical, as informed and voluntary as
is morally desirable and legally required will now construct their
requests for consent in such a way as to provide the opportunity
for potential subjects to take their time and consult others in
making decisions. We know of one distinguished South American medical research scientist who will not accept any subject
into his experiments on the efficacy and safety of long-acting
contraceptive implants until that subject has privately consulted
with some former subject in the experiments. Instead of creating
compliance based on ignorance and fear of scientific authority,
as Milgram has and as many medical experiments do, however
unwittingly, we can create the conditions for knowledgeable
and voluntary participation.

Incidentally, though he does not use certain of his findings to
make this argument, which would be contrary to his primary
thesis about the excessive psychological propensity of his subjects and of Americans in general to obedience to authority,
some of Milgram's own findings support the view that under the
appropriate social conditions his subjects, and presumably
others, are less obedient than they are when put into a situation
of social isolation. For example, Milgram found that the rate of
obedience among his subjects dropped when the authoritative
scientist-experimenter was not in the room, not face-to-face with
the subjects, but gave them his orders over the telephone instead. Authority is not entirely eliminated by telephonic remote-
ness; but it is reduced, perhaps because the individual subject feels less overawed by the scientist-experimenter. Milgram
also found that the rate of obedience dropped when he planted
two rebellious fake subjects in the room with the real subject.
When these fake subjects refused to obey the experimenter's

orders, the real subject took social and moral support from their disobedience and followed suit. These findings show that the authoritarianism of the doctor as scientist is strongly supported by the typical situation in which he confronts an isolated, frightened, and deferential patient.

The Social Sources of Medical Authoritarianism

If professional dominance is the prevalent pattern in the real medical world, as our sparse evidence seems to indicate, how shall we account for it? What are its social sources? We have rejected the hypothesis that transcendent medical authority is needed to overcome the consequences of structured medical uncertainty for physicians and patients. Routine and trivial complaints are probably far more frequent in medicine than really consequential uncertainty. We have also rejected the argument that physicians are too busy, because there is evidence that some doctors are idle enough to need to create work for themselves and because doctors' work loads could be reduced by effective delegation of tasks, a delegation physicians on the whole resist. We must look instead to the excessive authority doctors have assumed from the fact of their technical expertise—especially when technical expertise is expanded to include not only biological knowledge but, far more tenuously, social and moral knowledge. We must also look to the lack of effective medical self-regulation or control by outsiders over this excessive authority. These are the chief social sources of professional dominance. In Chapter 6, we shall come back to consider in detail the problems and evidence on medical self-regulation and "outside" lay control. We emphasize "outside" because it is only professional dominance that has defined laymen as outsiders. For better procedures of informed consent, they should be defined as "inside" the medical system, as colleagues rather than cases and subjects that are "out there."

The Dilemma of Authority and Equality

Present relationships between medical experts and their patients and subjects manifest a modern dilemma that is also found in many other areas of social relationships. This is the dilemma of authority and equality. Growing and changing claims to authority, whether based on office or on expertise, are often in conflict with or challenged by growing and changing claims to equality, voiced in the name of a value general and fundamental in our society. As a result, we face a continuous moral and policy challenge to accommodate these powerful but potentially conflicting claims. Obviously, we have to preserve the authority of genuine and inevitable authority, recognizing always that what we have thought genuine and inevitable in the past may not turn out to be so under the hard scrutiny of better social science research and analysis. Equally obviously, we seek to enlarge the spheres of equality as far as possible. A good deal of successful accommodation does in fact occur. For example, Sorenson has pointed out that many physicians acting as counselors to patients facing genetics problems for themselves or their children have retreated from unwarranted moral authoritarianism to the role of informants and teachers seeking to instruct their patients in the technical knowledge necessary for them to make their own decisions (1974). There is also much resistance to the innovations that better accommodation between authority and equality now require. For example, although a few physicians suggest that patients would be better informed if they had free access to their own medical records, most physicians apparently disapprove, without considering the potential advantages of such a new practice (see Chapter 5). We also find what we may call overreaching, rather than rational accommodation, in some proposed innovations for achieving a better balance between authority and equality. Suggestions by some women that they become their own gynecologists seem to have a quality of overreaching about them, an excessive intrusion on technical expertise. Overreaching is nevertheless to be expected in all areas of social and value change in the face of what is defined by the overreachers as overbearing authority. It may be overcome or reduced, however, just as blind resistance to change may also be overcome or reduced, if we are aware of its likelihood and of its social sources. We need to organize the knowledge and construct the social policy that most effectively cope with the dilemma of authority and equality through better accommodation rather than through conflict.

5

Communication and Informed Consent

Satisfactory informed consent obviously requires effective communication among the many different participants in what we have now seen are the complex subsystems of medical relationships, relationships often thought to include only doctor and patient or researcher and subject but actually including families, friends, medical colleagues, paramedicals, administrators, and other professionals such as social workers and genetic counselors. In the past three chapters, we have looked at some of the larger social system determinants of informed consent and communication patterns. We have seen how values and norms, legal principles and rules, and authority patterns affect processes of communication and informed consent. In Chapter 6, we shall consider further determinants from the larger social system on communication and the processes and outcomes of informed consent. In this chapter, we want to change focus and look directly at communication patterns in medical relationships. We want to inquire into the determinants, structures, and processes of the immediate communication situation. Besides being affected by larger system variables, communication is also partly an independent variable, with its own problems of structure and process. Although the larger system interacts with the immediate determinants of communication, both are important. Finally, we want to look in considerable detail at the actual outcomes of both sets of variables. We want to see what actual communications in medical relationships look like. What do we know about them? How effective do they seem to be? Serious deficiencies in their effectiveness are obviously consequential for achieving satisfactory informed consent. In this chapter then, while we recognize the danger of the analytic reductionism that says "communication is everything," we wish to give communication its due importance as a partly independent social variable.

SOME FUNCTIONS AND DILEMMAS OF COMMUNICATION

Communication among the participants in medical relationships has many functions, some of which are to inform the patient of the physician's diagnosis and prognosis; to try to obtain the patient's compliance with a therapeutic regimen; to persuade a patient or a normal volunteer to become a subject in an experiment; to instruct paramedicals and other professionals on how to assist the doctor, the patient, or the subject; to relieve the patient's anxiety and give him hope; and to inform collaborating specialists so that they can render effective service. Among and along with all these and other functions, the essential function of communication, so far as the matter of satisfactory informed consent is concerned, is telling the patient what he needs to know to make a competent, rational decision, acting as nearly as he can as a relative equal among equals in order to realize his own interests and values. A competent, rational decision depends upon the patient or subject being told what benefits he can expect, what risk of injury he runs, and what his alternatives are. A certain amount of information about the technical medical aspects of these benefits, risks of injury, and alternatives is necessary, but only insofar as it bears on the essential matter—the physiological, social, and moral consequences for the patient or subject. Indeed, we have suggested that there is a sense in which the physiological consequences are important only because they have social and moral consequences. In the extreme case, for example, the patient or subject is interested not in the physiological process of his own death but only in its social and moral meaning for him and for those in his morally meaningful social circles—those who share his essential activities in work, in friendship, in the family, and in the community.

By concentrating on this essential function of communication for informed consent, we see a number of general problems and dilemmas that need to be resolved before we proceed to our examination of the detailed evidence on patterns and processes of communication. For example, what is competence? What is rationality? Is informed consent easy or hard to obtain? How does more knowledge affect the patient's or subject's behavior? What of the wish, expressed by some patients or subjects, not to know as much as they might? Brief general statements on these dilemmas will be useful before we look at detailed evidence on communication in medical systems.

The Matter of "Competence"

It is often asserted or taken for granted in medical circles that the patient or subject is not competent to give informed consent to his participation in therapy or research. Professor Jay Katz, a psychiatrist and a professor at the Yale Law School, has observed that

> Significant disclosure is not standard practice for the vast majority of physicians. Indeed, disclosure and consent, except in the most rudimentary fashion, are obligations alien to medical practice. Doctors believe that patients are neither emotionally nor intellectually equipped to play a significant role in decisions affecting their medical fate, that they must be guided past childish fears into "rational" therapy, and that disclosures of uncertainty, gloomy prognosis and dire risks often seriously undermine cure (1977, p. 148).

Such assertions and assumptions neglect the fact that competence is a relative matter, determined in considerable measure by what is communicated and how. If a doctor or researcher communicates only esoteric technical information, then of course the layman is incompetent, by definition. But if the risks of injury, the benefits, and the alternative modes of treatment are presented in such a way that the adequately intelligent person can understand, then competence can exist. In short, competence can be created by some communications and made impossible by others. When the physician or researcher, for whatever reasons, either does not communicate with the patient or subject at all or does not communicate well, he is making a self-fulfilling prophecy that the patient is incompetent. When the physician communicates effectively, on the other hand, he creates competence by a different assumption and a different self-fulfilling prophecy.

The Matter of "Rationality"

We have said that the essential function of information for adequate informed consent is to provide the patient, subject, or volunteer with the information he needs to make a rational decision—a decision where he carefully weighs risks, benefits, and alternatives in the light of his interests and values. The common assumption, which is probably correct, is that such rational decisions in most therapeutic and experimental situations will take time, that the individual will have to assimilate the information given him and reflect on it as long as is necessary to weigh the alternatives laid before him. On such an assumption, a speedy, almost "automatic" consent is suspect, a product of "irrationality" rather than of careful rational thought.

How then do we respond to consent to a dangerous medical procedure where the individuals asked to undergo the procedure give their consent immediately and "automatically"? Fellner and Marshall have discovered such a situation in the case of potential kidney donors, individuals who have been asked to come to a hospital to be medically and psychologically evaluated as kidney donors for members of their immediate families (1970). Twenty such potential donors, interviewed by Fellner and Schwartz while still undergoing these protracted processes of evaluation, indicated that they "had made their decision immediately when the subject of the kidney transplant was first mentioned over the telephone, 'in a split second,' 'instantaneously,' and 'right away' " (1970, p. 1245). They did not wait to meet with the kidney transplant doctors to have all the relevant information and statistics about the risks put before them. They did not wait until they were tissue-typed, evaluated as to general physical health, or judged in terms of psychological fitness. They made their decisions without a moment's hesitation.

Fellner and Marshall call the decisions these donors made "irrational," but that seems to us to be an erroneous judgment. The case of the immediately consenting kidney donors is more sociologically interesting than such a judgment suggests. What this case represents is not an instance of ordinary, sociologically uninteresting "irrationality" but a demonstration of the sociologically interesting fact that "rationality" and "irrationality" are the results not merely of individual and psychological processes but of cultural and social structural determinants as well. The immediate consent of these donors was "rational" under the altruistic obligations of close kinship connections in our society. Short of death, and perhaps in some cases even up to that point, the needs of close kin are immediate and "automatic" obligations for us. We do not wait to calculate the details of risks, benefits, and alternatives. Indeed, the donors themselves recognized this socio-logic of rationality. "All our subjects," Fellner and Marshall say, "clearly expressed their opinion that this was a rather special situation that could not be compared to ordinary decision making (1970, p. 1246). In the great majority of therapeutic and experimental research situations, informed consent should not be immediate, uncalculated, and automatic. Careful communication, thought, time, and due process should occur. But there are some very special social situations in which a different logic of rationality applies. The difference highlights the ordinary situation and its ordinary, everyday logic. The processes of communication and decision will differ in the two situations.

It should be noted that it is for the individual subject or patient himself, not his doctor or researcher, to decide which pattern of obligation and which consequent logic of rationality applies. The doctor and researcher should proceed on the basis of ordinary logic, probably even when the patient or subject chooses, under special conditions, to apply a special kind of rationality. Proceeding always in the ordinary, calculating way, the doctor provides an extra safeguard for the patient, subject, or volunteer. The doctor proceeding on ordinary logic thus makes it clear to the patient or subject that it is for him and him alone to make his decision and on his own grounds.

The Matter of "Perfectionism"

In discussions of communications in medical relationships, a certain "perfectionism" is often expressed or implied, a set of excessive expectations or excessive fears about the consequences if perfect communication existed. (An example of excessive negative expectations can be found in Garnham. Garnham concludes that "informed consent is extraordinarily difficult to achieve; so much so as usually to be a practical impossibility in medically naive subjects" [1975, p. 145].) Perfect communication is a utopian ideal, something to be striven toward rather than likely to be achieved. Communication in medical relationships is definitely improvable, but even such improvements will not solve all problems for patients or doctors. Even with better communications, patients will still be frightened, their decisions will often be difficult to make, and they will often forget what they have been carefully told by the physician or researcher. Physicians sometimes object to better communication and better information on consent forms that they will "only" frighten the patient or subject. Unfortunately, in many ways the doctor may have to do frightening things or give frightening information to patients or subjects. Perfect communication does not consist of eliminating matters that are inevitably frightening. The physician cannot take unto himself such powers of altering reality. The patient must be told how matters really stand for him, unless he explicitly says he does not want to be told.

In an imperfect world, such knowledge will often not only frighten the patient but also make it hard for him to make a decision. Good communication does not always lead to easy decisions for the patient or subject. For example, as a result of all the controversy over the necessity for the present treatment of choice, radical mastectomy, for women with breast cancer, some physicians may feel obliged to acquaint their patients with this controversy and with the fact that none of the alternative treatments has ever been clearly shown to be superior to the others by carefully randomized and controlled trials (Crile, 1972). In this situation, better communication is probably more frightening and harder to cope with for some women and their husbands and more satisfactory for others, though we do not know how many would fall into each category. (See Crile, 1972, for some impressionistic evidence.) Radical mastectomy is only more extreme than many other surgical procedures, few of which have been tested by controlled trials. In all these cases, better communication and information will increase their troubles for some patients. It is clear that although better communication may be morally desirable, it will not create ease and perfection in the medical world.

Nor should physicians have excessive expectations concerning their patients' abilities to remember the details or, in extreme cases, even the facts presented through good communication processes. Startled by the discovery that several of their patients did not even remember the fact of an informed consent interview, two cardiac surgeons studied how much their patients remembered four to six months after these interviews (Robinson and Merav, 1976). Two days before scheduled major heart surgery, each patient, in a carefully structured but informal session with the surgeon, was given the following information: diagnosis of his illness; proposed operation, surgical techniques to be used, and possible prosthetic devices that might be necessary; risks; possible complications of surgery and prosthetic devices; benefits; and alternative treatments and their chances for success or failure. All the patients were asked several times during the dialogue if they had any questions. The interviews were recorded. All these patients were "experienced," having been previously hospitalized one or more times for diagnostic or therapeutic purposes. None of the operations was on an emergency basis.

Four to six months after these informed consent interviews and subsequent surgery, twenty patients were reinterviewed to test their recall of the original interviews. The findings "indicated generally poor retention in all categories of informed consent information. . . . Each of the twenty patients failed to recall major parts of the interview" (Robinson and Merav, 1976, p. 20). Four kinds of errors were made by the patients on reinterview: failure to recall; positive denial of a truth; fabrication or the assertion of a falsehood; and errors of attribution, that is, attributing information to the informed consent interview that was obtained by the patient subsequently from some other source. Despite all these errors and failures of memory, the researchers believe "that all patients completely understood the information given and gave a truly informed consent to surgery." They feel that their study "calls attention to the fact that, while these patients were well informed and comprehended prior to surgery, they subsequently forgot most of what they had understood and made other qualitative errors in their attempts to recall" (p. 21). Because of this, they believe that it is important to document, by taping or other means, the details of the communication process leading to informed consent and to make the documentation part of a permanent clinical record.

The Matter of Consequences for Consent

Among physicians, there is a widespread prejudice against providing full information in the belief that well-informed patients will refuse to consent to necessary procedures. One physician, who himself admits to having had this prejudice, reports that when he questioned a number of his colleagues about obtaining informed consent, their responses fell into three categories: (1) I always inform my patients; (2) I don't do it, it's a waste of time; and most frequently, (3) "If I give my patients a comprehensive explanation of what is to be done and what possible complications might ensue, the result would be the wholesale refusal of patients to undergo the procedure" (Alfidi, 1971, p. 1325). Believing that this was so, that if he told his patients about the pains and possible complications resulting from angiography (a procedure in which a tube is inserted into a blood vessel in either the arm or the groin by means of minor surgery under local anesthesia in order to study the blood vessels by X-ray after a solution has been introduced into them through the inserted tube) they would refuse to undergo the procedure, Dr. Alfidi designed a study to prove his prejudiced hypothesis. Much to his surprise, patients (for whom the procedure might be helpful) did not refuse angiography after they were informed in "straightforward and even harsh" terms of the possible complications resulting from the procedure. In all, 228 out of 232 gave their consent. Dr. Alfidi concludes that he has "proven that the majority of patients not only have a right to know but want to know what possible complications may be expected from any given procedure. The concern that informing the patient of possible complications will result in his refusal of the procedure is now outmoded" (1971, p. 1329).

Dr. Alfidi is perhaps a little premature. One case, one study, one procedure tested is not conclusive of his general assertion; but his remarkable study not only indicates the existence of medical prejudice against communicating with patients and obtaining informed consent for therapy but also offers strong evidence that the prejudice may be mistaken. We need more research of this kind on other medical procedures and in other medical situations. We cannot go to the opposite extreme from Dr. Alfidi's original view and assume that all patients in all situations want to be fully informed. A recent study by Jim McIntosh, a sociologist at the Institute of Medical Sociology in Aberdeen, Scotland, gives evidence on this latter point (*The Lancet*, August 7, 1976). McIntosh interviewed seventy-four patients with diagnosed but undisclosed cancer on a ward for the treatment of malignant disease in a Scottish hospital. McIntosh questioned them about their perceptions of their conditions and progress, their desire for additional information, and their success in obtaining it. Nine of the patients had no suspicion of malignancy on admission to the ward. The remaining sixty-five (88 percent) either suspected they had a malignancy (47) or stated they knew they had one (18). Of the forty-seven who suspected they had cancer, only fifteen wanted to know for sure. Of those sixty-five who suspected or knew their diagnosis, fifty "wished, or required no information on their diagnosis." Furthermore, "no patient wanted to know whether, or when, the illness was likely to prove fatal." These results may be as extreme on the other side as Alfidi's were for wanting to know. Certainly they show that more information is not always wanted by all patients. Again, we can only remind ourselves that we need a good deal more research to discover when and how patients want to be fully informed. The presumption should always be in favor of as much information as patients and subjects want, but some investigation into just what constitutes this amount would result in more satisfactory communication and informed consent.

THE ACCESSIBILITY OF PHYSICIANS AND RESEARCHERS

We turn now from our attempt to resolve certain general problems of medical communication to somewhat more specific topics. One of these is the matter of the accessibility of physicians and researchers for effective communication with their patients and subjects. Though accessibility, both actual physical accessibility and the style of behavior that makes easy patient access seem welcome to the physician, is obviously an important determinant of communication processes, we have little systematic evidence about it. Once again, we must rely on the informal "murmuring of the masses" that expresses the complaints and grievances of patients who feel that their doctors are not accessible enough, either physically or in manner. Patients commonly complain that it is difficult to reach their physicians quickly or easily on the phone. Medical secretaries seem trained to be off-putting. When they take phone messages, physicians do not return them quickly. Patients also complain about long waiting times for appointments, inconvenient and unpredictable attendance in waiting rooms and clinics, and the general brusqueness and uncommunicativeness of physicians once one is actually in their presence. All of this is contrasted to a myth about the past, equally unsupported by good evidence, that the doctor of old was always and easily "there," both in person and in his receptive manner. The key symbol of the change from the old pattern of accessibility to the new, perhaps, is the house call. The mythological picture of the old type physician has him not only making house calls regularly but even sitting by the bedside. The new physician makes no house calls; and he is alleged to be barely approachable even in his office.

Nor does the situation seem to be better for the physician-researcher and his subjects. Communicating with subjects and obtaining their informed consent is too often left to nurses and juniors; it is not the immediate responsibility of the senior physician, the principal investigator himself. Problems of responsibility for obtaining satisfactory informed consent may be especially difficult in hospitals. As a result of his observational study of informed consent processes in a psychiatric hospital, Zerubavel has argued that the bureaucratic segmentation and disper-sonalization of medical care and research in large hospitals often leads inevitably to a "floating responsibility" that inheres in no single person and therefore finally settles in the interstices among all persons. "That the patient is left uninformed or only inadequately informed is highly characteristic of a context within which no one is fully and exclusively responsible for any particular patient" (1977, p. 23). In very special, highly innovative experiments, exceptions occur (see Fox, 1959); but ordinarily, impression has it, communication and informed consent in the research situation are seen as relatively unimportant routine formalities. (For some good evidence, though, see Carlton, 1978.) Not that the busy principal investigator need always be in actual and prolonged communication with his subjects. In many situations, this can be left to well-instructed, conscientious as-sistants to the principal investigator after he has made his own responsible investigation and trial of the consent problem. Communication can be responsibly delegated, but only on the same grounds as treatment would be.

VOCABULARIES OF ILLNESS

One of the chief obstacles to effective communication in medical relationships arises because the different participants often have different vocabularies of illness and health, different languages that impede communication among them rather than facilitate it. On this matter we have an abundance of good evi-dence. In one study of both doctors and their urban and rural patients in a Scottish hospital clinic, appraisals were made of the extent to which the two different groups agreed or disa-greed in their understanding of terms that are commonly used during medical examinations (Boyle, 1970). The terms were both technical and nontechnical, symptomatic and anatomical, including *arthritis, heartburn, palpitation, the heart, the kidneys,* and *good appetite.* There were 35 physicians and 234 adult pa-tients in a variety of ambulatory clinics who responded to the questionnaire testing their knowledge and understanding. The doctors showed a high, though incomplete consensus on defi-nitions, of course; but this was not so for the patients. Between 80 and 90 percent of the patients could give a correct definition for *a good appetite, arthritis, heartburn,* and *bronchitis;* but fewer than a majority could correctly define *a medicine, flatulence,* and *diarrhea.* They also showed "a considerable lack of knowledge of simple anatomy." Indeed, "the difference between the 'majority doctors' definition' and the number of patients agreeing with that definition was significant for all terms and illustrations except the term 'a good appetite.' " And Boyle concludes, "For the clinician the results probably do no more than formalize and lend statistical verification to his impression that clinical interrogation often reveals large areas of misunderstanding between conventional medical opinion and the vagaries of the lay mind" (1970, p. 289). Just how many clinicians are aware of this impression and act to improve communications, this study does not say; but it does go on to warn that programs that use patient self-completion questionnaires or patient-activated computer programs as diagnostic supplements should take these demonstrated differences in the understanding of medical terms into account.

In another study, carried out in an American hospital clinic, the level of medical information about ten common diseases in a group of 214 unselected medical outpatients was investigated (Seligmann, McGrath, and Pratt, 1957). For each disease, questions were asked about etiology, symptoms, and treatment. Of the answers given to the test questions appraising level of information, 45 percent were incorrect. "It is clear from the foregoing," the researchers conclude, "that persons in the study were poorly and irregularly informed about disease" (p. 509). It is interesting that the researchers found patients knew more about those diseases that had been the subjects of intensive education programs, indicating that it is possible to improve patient knowledge about health and illness and suggesting that perhaps more could be done by the treating physician himself.

Findings from a comprehensive study of patterns of communication between pediatricians and the mothers of their patients in the emergency clinic at Childrens Hospital of Los Angeles further define the way in which misunderstandings and ignorance on the part of patients and their adult surrogates prevent effective medical communication (Korsch, Gozzi, and Francis, 1968; see also Freeman et al., 1971, for another report from this research). In this case, the researchers both recorded the medical interviews and conducted followup interviews with

eight hundred mothers who had participated in patient visits.
"One of the striking findings consistently demonstrated in all
phases of the study," the researchers found, "is the patients'
intense concern with and need for information and explanation
of their child's disease and what caused it" (p. 298). Although
the majority of these mothers expressed overall satisfaction with
their communication with their doctors, "an outstanding barrier
to communication encountered in more than half the recorded
cases is the pediatrician's use of difficult technical language"
(p. 311). One mother, in an interview, said the doctor talked
"medical," and another mother, during her interaction with him,
requested her doctor to repeat what he had said in "English."
There were mothers who could not understand technical terms
used to apply to the child's anatomy (e.g., nares, labia, sphinc-
ter), to physiological processes (e.g., ingestion, edema, peristal-
sis), to laboratory procedures (e.g., lumbar puncture, Coomb's
titre, Tine test), "and to the many other subjects dealt with in
medical consultations." The researchers found a great many
instances in the tape recordings of the medical visits in which a
special language of the hospital, "a routine stereotyped language" not understood by the mothers, was used. Words like
"workup," "follow," and "history" are, they say, often "as
obscure to the patient as fancy technical terms, and they are
used ceaselessly by the medical staff without finding out
whether the patient understands. One mother told the inter-
viewer that the doctor said they would "admit her for a work-
up—whatever that means" (p. 300). It was not clear to the
mother that this meant hospitalization of the child.

This study points out with great insight the way in which vi-
cious cycles occur in communications between doctor and patient or patient surrogate. Defects on either side of the transaction result in a worsening of the process for the other party. "If
the doctor fails repeatedly to heed her statement of some basic
worry or of her main hopes and expectations from him, she may
'cease to try' as evidenced by the fact that she either becomes
completely mute or reduces her answers to toneless 'hmms' and
'yeses.' Things said and done by the doctor after this critical
point may not even be perceived by the mother"(p. 308). Even
when there is clear documentation to the contrary in the recordings of the medical interviews, in these instances the mother will
say, "the doctor did not even examine her," or, "he didn't tell

me what was the matter." Sometimes it is the doctor who gives up when the mother is communicating in a "disturbed, verbose, or unreasonable" way. "This is demonstrated in that his answers to the mother become decreasingly meaningful and less related to what the mother is saying" (p. 308).

Finally, the researchers suggest that many physicians engage in a process that has been called "patient culpability," that is, blaming poor communication entirely on such patient attributes as socioeconomic background, education, or ethnic and racial background. The authors feel that the effect of these factors "has probably been overestimated" and that more attention should be paid to physician defects in communication. They feel that "important and highly relevant information concerning patient fears and expectations is readily obtainable with the simplest interview questions" and that "currently these concerns are given insufficient attention during doctor–patient communications." They indicate that some of their data show that effective communication from the doctor "makes for shorter patient visits" and more patient satisfaction.

In addition to general communication difficulties all patients may experience as a result of nearly universal ignorance or misunderstanding in the laity, there are differences in knowledge and understanding between different types of patients that physicians need to know about for effective communication. For example, one study showed that women who presented themselves with similar kinds of discomfort to a psychiatric clinic described their troubles in quite different ways, depending on their education and social class position (Bart, 1968). The better educated women, married to professionals or other higher status men, were more likely to be aware of the possible psychogenic origins of their symptoms than the poorly educated, lower class women. The less educated women tended to "somatize" their troubles, to look for hysterectomies as solutions rather than for psychiatric aid.

Considering this considerable problem of different languages for illness and health on the part of many patients and doctors, it is not surprising that we occasionally should find various kinds of medical specialists becoming aware of these problems in their field. "We have been concerned," say two cardiologists in a special commentary in the *Journal of the American Medical Association,* "about the diagnostic terms that colleagues use when describing cardiac disease to their patients. Despite their efforts to be scrupulously honest in their explanations, the technical words they often use may fail to convey an actual understanding of the condition and may even mislead the patient and evoke unnecessary and even devastating anxiety" (Blacher and Levine, 1976, p. 1699). For example, they suggest that when a doctor dispenses digitalis for the condition often referred to in medical jargon as "heart failure" he should avoid this "terrifying" term and tell the patient instead that the "heart muscle is a bit tired and lacks the normal vigor of contraction." Or, instead of speaking technically of "atrial fibrillation," he might tell patients that "they are being treated for variations in their cardiac rhythm." With patients who seem to know the technical diagnosis already, they suggest that the doctor should question their interpretation of the words to see if they are in error or fear. In sum, they conclude, "a description that neither describes nor reassures is not a useful part of the physician's lexicon" (1976, p. 1699).

The entrapment of physicians and patients in their separate languages has also been noted and studied by some sociolinguists, scholars who have a special competence in investigating the functions and consequences of a wide variety of social dialects. (See Shuy, 1972; 1973; and Shuy and Rubin, 1973; see also Kimball, 1971, for at least one doctor's awareness of "dialect" problems.) These sociolinguists have made beginning studies both of face-to-face interviews at Georgetown University Hospital and of the questions asked in various computerized programs used to acquire medical information from patients. "The content and wording of the questions" used in these programs, they say, "may be assumed to be representative of the more individualized and time-consuming patient–doctor communication" (Shuy, 1973, p. 3). In both types of communication, they find that "the concepts and the language of such questions are clearly middle-class, uninvolved, and jargonish." They were especially concerned about the "middle-class" aspect of the physicians' language because most of the patients were black, inner-city ghetto residents with a phonology, lexicon, and grammar different from those of the physicians. In addition to studying face-to-face interviews and computer program questions, Shuy asked a random group of eighty-six patients in the waiting rooms of the various clinics and private medical practices in the hospital to respond to a questionnaire about their communication experiences and satisfaction. The results, he says, "demonstrate clear evidence of how widespread" the problem of poor understanding and ineffective communication is (Shuy, 1973, p. 20). In the matter of vocabulary, for example, 41 percent of the respondents, varying by both race and sex, "said that they sometimes felt the doctor did not understand the patient's problem." Thirty-eight percent of the respondents "thought that doctors, nurses or interns sometimes use words that are difficult to understand"; an equal number felt "it was sometimes difficult for the patient to explain himself to the doctor" and "would prefer the doctor to speak in simpler language." In this study, 41 percent "felt inhibited by the doctor's attitude, personality or style." Finally, 70 percent of the respondents believed that sometimes "the doctor withholds information they think they should know" (p. 21). In summary, Shuy says:

> We can safely generalize that the doctors do not speak patient language and, much more seriously, that they often give little evidence of understanding it. They are not especially friendly, not very good at making the patient comfortable, and generally lack expertise at question-asking. The patient generally adjusts to the doctor perspective, offering medical terms whenever possible. When the patient cannot do this well, the history is slowed and made less efficient. In short, the general expectation is for the patient to learn doctor talk (1973, p. 25).

Physicians could do much to improve medical communication.

COMPLIANCE STUDIES

In the days before the emergence of scientific medicine, when the drugs and regimens doctors prescribed for their patients were almost never powerfully specific remedies, there was little systematic concern with whether or not patients complied with these regimens, although clearly noncompliance did occur. Not taking medicines may be as old as medicine itself. In the Hippocratic writings there is the following statement: "[The physician] should keep aware of the fact that patients often lie when they state that they have taken certain medicines" (Cited in Lasagna, 1973). Doctors, then as now, tended to blame the patient. Beginning in the period after World War II, when more specific and powerful remedies such as the antibiotics became available, physicians became actively concerned with the degree of patient compliance with the instructions for using these drugs and their associated dietary regimens. From the 1950s on, this concern, reflected in the cooperation of social researchers from the emerging field of medical sociology, produced a small flood of "compliance studies" which tried to find out to what extent and why patients did or did not take their medicines. For the first fifteen years or so, the predominant assumption of these compliance studies was that noncompliance was attributable to some characteristics of the patient, some defects in his behavior. For example, the report on a typical compliance study from the early 1960s begins in this way:

> The successful application of ambulatory or home-care programs for the control of desease demands that the physician be able to detect those persons who will, and those who will not, take self-medication as prescribed. Ultimately, by recognition of certain characteristics or personality traits, the physician may be able to detect the potentially unreliable patient before treatment is begun (Schwartz et al., 1962, p. 2018).

This individualistic, nonsystemic approach tended to blame the "unreliable" or "uncooperative" patient. Since then, however, there has been a shift away from the "patient culpability" assumption to a more social system approach, studying the interaction among doctor, patient, and other participants in the medical system. This new approach assumes that some considerable cause of patient compliance or noncompliance is the doctor's communication behavior—how and what he tells the patient what he wants him to do to help himself.

Just how much noncompliance with prescribed regimens is there? One review of the literature reported "a range from 15 to 93% of patients reportedly noncompliant" (Davis, 1968). This wide range, says Davis, "is not surprising when the variety of populations, the various methods of data collection, and the different medical problems investigated are considered. Nevertheless, a pattern emerges when these studies are examined as a whole. Regardless of the differences, at least a third of the patients in most studies failed to comply with doctors' orders" (p. 115). Another report seems to agree with this rough estimate. Blackwell says, "A recent review of over 50 studies found that complete failure to take medication often occurred in between one-quarter and one-half of all outpatients" (1973, p. 249). Besides complete failure to take medicines or follow other prescribed regimens, there are a number of other types of noncompliance or errors in following doctors' prescriptions. Some patients take prescribed medicines for the wrong reason, or they make errors in dosage or in timing, or they even mistakenly take medications that have not been prescribed by their physicians. Some patients commit several of these mistakes at the same time.

Under the older assumption of compliance studies, the fault lay primarily in the patient, a wide variety of factors was studied as possible determinants of noncompliance. Among these were type and seriousness of illness; the patient's age, sex, marital status, household composition, education, economic condition, and ethnic affiliation; the type of prescribed regimen, whether single or multiple medications, and whether single or frequent dose routines; the occurrence of side effects; the size, shape, and color of pills (see Mazullo, 1972); and whether or not the patient is allowed to obtain and read the package insert that comes to the pharmacist with his medications (Brody, 1976). By the late 1960s, Davis's studies of the so-called "demographic" or "background" factors in noncompliance convinced him that they were not important determinants of this behavior. As he put it, "No variation in the disparity between attitudinal and behavioral compliance could be attributed to patient age, sex, race, marital status, religion, education, or occupation" (1967, p. 265). As we shall see, this made him turn his attention to communication processes between doctors and patients. Other studies besides Davis's have also found that the background characteristics of patients were not very important in accounting for noncompliance (Francis, Korsch, and Morris, 1969). Some tentative findings apart from communication difficulties have nevertheless emerged from compliance studies. In his review of the literature, Blackwell describes the set of characteristics and conditions in which a patient is more likely to be "at risk" of noncompliance:

> those with chronic illnesses requiring long-term maintenance, with suppressive or preventive treatment. . . . Children, the elderly, and the disadvantaged can cooperate less readily. Patients with hostile feelings toward doctors or those with risk-taking,

obsessional, paranoid, or hypochondriacal personalities may be unwilling to comply. The patient will be more likely to take medication prescribed by a familiar, well liked physician who believes in the importance of medication and adopts a reassuring attitude to treatment or side effects. Finally, medication is more likely to be taken if the number of drugs is few, the frequency of taking them is less, and the side effects are minimal. Those who are most closely supervised in the hospital or at home are more likely to comply (1973, p. 252).

Let us now look at several studies, beginning with Davis's, that have demonstrated the importance of communication difficulties in regimen noncompliance. Presumably these same difficulties would be important in obtaining informed consent for either therapy or research participation. Davis's study group consisted of 154 new patients and the 76 junior physicians (fourth-year medical students who regularly care for patients in the clinics) and 78 senior (attending) physicians who saw them in a general medical clinic in a large voluntary teaching hospital (1968). Interactions between doctor and patient, some 223 of them, were studied by the Bales interaction process analysis method, by interviews with doctors and patients, and by survey questionnaires. Compliance was measured by a variety of objective and subjective (attitudinal) measures combined into an index. In this study, 37 percent of the patients were noncompliant. There was "no significant relationship between compliance and any of the demographic characteristics investigated." Instead, communication problems were found to be the source of noncompliance. Compliance was greater if the physician had given suggestions and information and if the patient had asked for the physician's suggestions and opinions or expressed agreement or revealed any tension. Noncompliance was more likely among patients who showed but did not express tension and when the doctor asked for information from the patient but did not provide feedback.

A review of a half-dozen or more studies of efforts to obtain patient compliance with medication regimens for control of hypertension not only points to the importance of communication problems but specifies some of the ways in which communication between medical personnel and patients can be improved: "General information about blood pressure, by itself probably has little effect on most patients' pill-taking compliance or on long-term blood pressure control" (Podell and Gary, 1976, p. 1121). They describe one controlled study in which a group of industrial workers with high blood pressure were given an excellent teaching program with quizzes to make sure that the information was learned. A control group received none of this teaching. After six months, the rates of non-compliance were the same in both groups. What did make a difference, another controlled study showed, was adding a whole set of specific informational interventions by the pharmacist investigator to the general information. This investigator not only gave one of his two groups general information about high blood pressure but also "discussed specific details of the current regimen, clarified the physician's instructions, questioned the patients about compliance, sought out complications and medication side effects, and recommended therapeutic changes to the physician based upon the patient's response and compliance" (1976, p. 1121). In the group of patients getting all this informational intervention, the proportion taking their medication increased from 25 to 79 percent. The controls, those not getting this intervention, showed no change in compliance. Compliance in the intervention group dropped when the intervention stopped, showing the necessity for continued communication with patients who are on prolonged medical regimens if compliance is to occur. It should be noted that in this study the intervention was carried out by a pharmacist, not by the treating physician. All of the intervention activities—clarifying instructions, monitoring compliance, eliciting negative feedback, adjusting the medical regimen—say Podell and Gary "could and should also be carried out by the physician." Nonetheless, it is also clear that physician substitutes, in cooperation with the treating physician, can also be effective in improving communication and regimen compliance.

The studies reported by Davis and described by Podell and Gary were all carried out in institutional settings—in hospital clinics, neighborhood health centers, work sites, or specialized hypertension clinics. Yet most medical care is still carried on by doctors in private practice. The special interest of a study by Hulka and her colleagues is that it was carried out in the latter type of setting, among the patients of a stratified random sampling of all internists and family physicians in Fort Wayne, Indiana, with a population in its metropolitan area of about two hundred thousand (Hulka et al., 1976). The Hulka study included 357 patients and 46 physicians, 33 of them in family practice, the other 13 being internists. These two kinds of physicians are the main providers of primary care. The patients for this study suffered either from congestive heart failure (123 patients) or from diabetes mellitus (234 patients), two medical conditions frequently seen in the offices of primary care physicians that usually require one or more medications for their effective control. Patient compliance was measured by a variety of observational and questionnaire indicators applied by a nurse-interviewer during a visit to each patient's home a couple of weeks after the patient's visit to the doctor's office. Data were collected from doctor–patient pairs, and the following four distinctive types of medication error for each pair could occur: omission rate (proportion of drugs prescribed by the physician that the patient was not taking), commission rate (proportion of drugs being taken that physician had not prescribed), scheduling misconception rate (proportion of prescribed drugs taken by patient for which he did not know correct schedule), and scheduling noncompliance rate (proportion of prescribed drugs taken for which patient knew correct rate but did not follow it).

Drug error rates were about the same for patients with both types of disease; and for both, the error rates were important. As the investigators sum up, "With the exception of scheduling non-compliance, the magnitude of each type of error is appreciable. On the average patients are omitting 18–19 percent of drugs prescribed, *and* taking 19–20 percent more drugs than their physicians realize, *and* making scheduling errors on about 17 percent of drugs. Since each patient may be subject to more than one type of error, the cumulative effect of these errors may be profound" (Hulka et al., 1976, p. 27).

Before looking at communication difficulties as the source of these errors, Hulka and her colleagues looked at other possible causes. They found that none of the usual demographic variables were related to error rates nor was severity of disease. Error rates did increase with increasing number of drugs involved, though these error rates were lower for a given number of drugs when all drugs were scheduled on a once-a-day basis. Turning to communication defects, the investigators devised a communication score to measure communication effectiveness between doctor and patient. They found that "when patients were informed as to what was expected of them, their behaviors conformed to the expectation more than 85 percent of the time. The major problem was communication; a third or more of patients were unaware of the expectation in specific instructional areas." Their findings suggest "that non-informative physicians may be a greater problem than non-compliant patients. If instructions are to be followed, they must be understood by the patient. This may require written instructions or an additional provider to insure comprehension of the information transmitted" (1976, p. 30). They feel that "opportunities to enhance functional knowledge start with the physician at the time of initial prescribing, can be reinforced by the pharmacist at the time the prescription is filled, and should be continued by the physician or other provider at follow-up visits. Follow-up visits would be more effective if medications were physically present in order that both physician and patient could clearly visualize which drugs were being taken for which purpose" (p. 30). This study shows that doctors do not adequately explain the nature of the illnesses they treat and the function of each drug they prescribe for those illnesses.

A final study that illuminates the defects of medical communication processes has been reported by Bonnie Svarstad (1976). Svarstad studied a model neighborhood health center utilized by poor patients, many of whom were black or Puerto Rican. Her methods included systematic observation of actual physician–patient interaction, review of medical records and pharmacy files, follow-up interviews with the patients, and validation of their reports through a "bottle check." Svarstad reports that she started "with some of the same unwarranted assumptions" used in previous research, namely, that doctors' instructions would be "simple and unambiguous" and that the patients, after receiving verbal instructions and printed information on their medication containers "would know what the physicians expected them to do." She found that patients often left the clinic with a poor understanding of what the physicians expected them to do, and justifiably so. She says, "even though I had observed the clinic visit, reviewed the record, and examined carbon copies of the prescription forms, I was often confused" as to what the physician expected (p. 244).

She then looked for and found a series of shortcomings in the communication process. "First, it was evident that the physicians frequently did not discuss their expectations in an explicit manner. Of the 347 drugs prescribed or proscribed, 60 were never discussed during the observed visits. The physicians gave explicit, verbal advice about how long to take a drug in only 10 per cent of the 347 drug cases. How regularly the drug should be used was made explicit in about 17 percent of the cases. In addition, several physicians discussed certain dosage schedules ambiguously"(p. 225). Second, patients did not always receive printed instructions or written reminders of what was expected. Changes were sometimes made in established regimens without any record of the change for the patient. Medication containers often did not say for how long the drug was to be taken. "Of the 97 drugs dispensed for symptomatic relief, only 42 were dispensed with labels that noted that the drug should be taken 'as necessary' or 'as needed.' " One physician explained, "I don't always write that, but that's what I *mean*." A third communication problem lay in the disparities between the physicians' prescription request forms and the actual medication labels. Of the 179 drugs for which comparisons were possible, there was an inconsistency in 20 percent of the cases. Here is a situation in which the pharmacist contributes to the communication problem. Pharmacists sometimes omitted a statement of the symptom or condition being treated from the medication label, despite the doctor's orders. Finally, "an examination of the verbal and written instructions showed that in 29 per cent of the cases the physicians gave no information about the purpose and/or names of the drug." Instead, they would refer to something so vague as "little white pills," though a patient might have several medications that roughly corresponded to that description.

In summary, while some patients received adequate instructions on medication regimens, more did not. Using an index made up of the number of verbal and written instructions to patients, Svarstad found that 48 patients received "high instruction" and 83 received "low instruction." Many patients made errors as a result of this inadequate instruction. Out of 131 patients, 68 made at least one error in describing what the physician expected; and patient understanding and perception affected compliance with doctors' orders. Of those who had a complete understanding, 60 percent complied fully; of those who made at least one error in perception of what the doctor had said, only 17 percent complied. Patients who had received "high instruction" were more likely not only to understand but also to comply. Svarstad's study clearly shows the importance of good communication by the doctor for informed patient participation in effective medical relationships. As an insightful physician has put it, "The most important contribution to compliance is the understanding a patient has of the illness, the need for treatment, and the likely consequences of both. Time spent in explaining these issues pays multiple dividends, not least in the sense of alliance that emerges when patient and physician believe they are collaborating" (Blackwell, 1973).

PHYSICIAN AWARENESS OF PATIENT CONCERNS

One important reason for poor communication between doctors and patients is physicians' unawareness of their patients' concerns. In the 1950s, when several leading medical schools were trying to make their students more aware of patients' concerns through an innovative teaching program called comprehensive care, in which the students were trained to know about and care for "the whole patient" and his family, not just physiologically but socially and psychologically as well, a pair of investigators seeking to justify this new program made a study of surgical interns and residents in a large municipal teaching hospital to see how much they needed such a program (Brant and Kutner, 1957). Under the supervision of attending senior physicians, these interns and residents had "a large measure of responsibility for all phases of patient care, ranging from admission and diagnosis to work-up, carrying out medical and surgical procedures, to convalescent care in the hospital and eventual discharge" (p. 703). Interviews with the patients and residents and interns, and observation of their actual interaction, showed that these physicians showed little concern for and less awareness of their patients' questions, worries, and fears: "In general, house staff physicians on the surgical service do not often conceive of the physician–patient relationship as an integral, important, part of their role" (p. 706). The investigators recommend the kinds of changes in medical education that were to be included in the new comprehensive care programs, chief among which were teaching the student to see the patient as a "whole person" and to search out his basic social and psychological concerns. Unfortunately, in the competition with heavy emphasis in medical education on scientific medicine, the comprehensive care programs have been diluted or wholly eliminated from the medical curriculum. That there is still need for more teaching about awareness of the patient's concerns has been shown by Wendy Carlton's year-long participant-observation study of the training of medical students in "Midwest University Hospital Center" (Carlton, 1978). Professor Carlton's main finding is stated in the subtitle of her book, *The Primacy of Clinical Judgment over Moral Choice*. Attending physicians, residents, and interns, both in their own clinical actions and in the clinical teaching of their medical students, all concentrate on the specific disease, the specific biomedical symptom, not on the patient as a "whole person," even though the official catalogue of the medical school explicitly states that the treatment of the "whole person" is what the student is supposed to learn. In response to those who suggested that the 1960s and the subsequent period might have produced a "new medical student," Carlton's data offer negative findings. The present and continuing system of medical care has overpowered new impulses to be more directly and self-consciously concerned about the social and ethical aspects of medical care.

This lack of effective concern on the part of many physicians was demonstrated again in one part of the set of studies to which we have already referred that were carried out at Childrens Hospital in Los Angeles (Freeman et al., 1971). Using tape recordings of actual interactions and interviews with treating physicians and the mothers of their pediatric patients, the investigators discerned a number of what they called "blocks" to effective communication, some of which involved disregard or lack of awareness of patient concerns. For example, the transcripts of the recorded interactions showed that physicians were often "not listening" in a variety of ways, by "ignoring the patient's comments and switching to another subject" or by replying to some expression of patient concern "with vague comments or generalizations, [or] volunteering little or no concrete information." Furthermore, "often hospital personnel utter a series of questions without pausing for answers" (p. 300).

In recognition of and in response to this problem, Hulka and her colleagues devised a useful technique for measuring physicians' awareness of patient concerns that promises some help in alleviation of this problem (Hulka et al., 1970). Using the latest methods known in the field of attitude scale measurement,

Hulka and her colleagues worked out a set of statements that actual clinic and private patients used to express their central concerns about two conditions frequently presented to physicians, pregnancy and infant care: "In pregnancy, these concerns include the general emotional reaction to being pregnant, desirability of having the baby, fear of an abnormal baby, concern over loss of attractiveness, and concern over events occurring during childbirth" (p. 429). The items on infant care "related to growth and development, the mother's feelings of adequacy or inadequacy, and her attitude toward the baby's behavior and health" (p. 429). The final two sets of statements, or questionnaires, were presented both to the treating physicians and to their patients in three general practices in three different eastern states. One was a solo practitioner, another was a three-man group, and the third was a five-man group. Patients were given the questionnaires to express their concerns while waiting for treatment. Each physician also filled out the same questionnaire for each patient. He was asked not only to decide his patient's concerns as he saw them but also to predict how each patient would respond on her questionnaire. Some 117 patients were involved in this test. The findings showed a considerable amount of physician awareness of patient concerns, but the investigators were more interested in the fact that the test showed the general "feasibility of measuring physician awareness of patients' attitudes." They intend to test this technique further "in different types of practices serving populations with varying characteristics." With the aid of such social science techniques as these, we will learn more specifically and practically how to improve doctors' awareness of patient concerns and the overall effectiveness of medical communications. Such techniques are the necessary instruments for better compliance and better informed consent in both therapy and research.

GIVING THE PATIENT
HIS RECORD

Although physicians often communicate unsatisfactorily with their patients, they do create a large amount of information about each patient for their own present and future guidance, and presumably for the guidance of other doctors who may succeed them in treating the patient. This information is stored in each patient's medical record, and in many cases these records are voluminous indeed. But the patient's record is not for the patient's eye, and even other physicians often have difficulty in obtaining access to it. In this situation, it would be a radical change to let the patient see and keep his own medical record. Just such a suggestion has been made by two physicians from New Haven, Drs. Shenkin and Warner, in the *New England Journal of Medicine*, the most prestigious and authoritative general medical journal in the United States (1973). Their suggestion and some of the letters of response to the *Journal* tell us a good deal about physicians' views on communicating with patients. They also show how changed communication patterns and processes in the medical system affect all its many different dimensions, such as authority patterns, values, and social control mechanisms.

Drs. Shenkin and Warner preface their proposal that patients be "given copies of all their medical records" with the hope that the "serious problems" involved in "establishing mutually satisfactory physician–patient relations" could be "alleviated, in part" by doing so. Apart from such expected benefits, however, they also feel that it is the patient's right to have his record to be able to evaluate his medical service either on his own or with the help of experts of his own choosing, just as he has the right to evaluate other services he seeks and buys. "At present," they say, "medical records are not routinely available to either physicians or patients. In theory, records are transferable within the profession; in practice, they are seldom transferred even in summary form, and even within one institution" (p. 688). In nearly all states, there are laws that make it impossible for patients to obtain their records except through litigation. These laws, it should be noted, have been written on the advice and with the encouragement of the organized medical profession, which is powerful in all states in all matters having to do with medical legislation. Only three states "explicitly or implicitly allow direct access by the patient himself" (p. 689). In some of the letters of response to the Shenkin and Warner article, it was pointed out that patients carry their own medical records or have full access to them in such places as China, the Province of Quebec, East Africa, and a few hospitals in Vermont and Philadelphia (Letters, *New England Journal of Medicine*, 290[1974], 287–288).

Drs. Shenkin and Warner's detailed proposal has few qualifications. "We propose that legislation be passed to require that a complete and unexpurgated copy of all medical records, both inpatient and outpatient, be issued routinely and automatically to patients as soon as the services provided are recorded. The legislation should also require that physician and hospital qualifications (accreditations, memberships, etc.) and charges for services be recorded. Hospital records should be available regularly to patients on the ward, and copies sent to them upon termination of the hospitalization." A patient would have the option "to refuse or accept the record anonymously." They feel that the "proposal would benefit most participants in the medical-care system," not just patients, but doctors and also planners and administrators (p. 690).

How would it help patients? First of all, by improving communications between them and their physicians. "At present, patients generally receive insufficient information on their own case, and their health knowledge is quite poor regardless of socioeconomic status, race, rural or urban background, age group, or sex. Both physicians and patients find this undesirable" (p. 690). They feel that more information would reduce patient noncompliance and would be "a source of satisfaction in itself." By studying his record, the patient could supplement his memory of what the doctor told him and be able to "understand the rationale for treatment." The patient might be enabled "to keep relevant symptomatic notes for the next visit," thus making him a more effective cooperator with the physician. Shenkin and Warner stress the functions of the patient's having his medical record as "an educational tool." Patients might "consult books or medical personnel about unfamiliar words, and thus learn professional terminology and concept. Eventually, increased knowledge would lead to more appropriate utilization of physicians and a greater ability of patients to participate in their own care" (p. 690). It would make unnecessary the present situation in which the mobile patient has to give his history over and over again in each new medical encounter. The patient would be subjected to fewer repeat tests, would "receive more complete, better informed care [and] at all times feel just 'lost' in the system." The patient would be able to make better judgments about his physician and "to choose and change physicians more easily." Shenkin and Warner do not expect that the patient could do all this entirely on his own. They expect that "published guides to medical care would soon flourish, and professional consultant services for records, 'translation,' interpretation, and evaluation would arise in response to consumer demand" (p. 690). Such consultant services could be provided by medical societies, universities, and private groups, "which would then function as non-compulsory quality-enforcement mechanisms." The "profound dependency" of the patient would no longer be necessary; he could be more autonomous, as "American cultural norms" prescribe. Being more autonomous, patients would not only lose their current distrust for physicians but "physician–patient communication would improve. All these improvements would produce more harmonious physician–patient relations" (p. 691). Altogether, Shenkin and Warner thus expect fundamental, ramifying, and beneficial consequences from the patient's having his own medical record.

How would it affect the physician? Again, they predict beneficial effects on the whole. By seeing the records constructed by other physicians, a physician would have "new opportunities to learn." At the same time, such mutual scrutiny of each other's performance would provide a necessary process of "decentralized peer review." And, "anticipating this process, physicians would have a clear incentive to practice high-quality medicine." Finally, "improved physician–patient relations would add importantly to physician satisfaction " (p. 691).

Last, with the patient having and understanding his own record, there would be benefits for medical planners and administrators. Shenkin and Warner feel that

> at the present, power in the health system is decentralized to the penultimate step—the physician. In the eyes of planners, administrators, fiscal intermediaries and the public they represent, the physicians' autonomy is unchecked. Administrators and policy makers do not have the capacity easily to evaluate or control the appropriateness of medical care (p. 691).

To make such evaluations and get such control, planners and administrators have been driven to use heavy-handed bureaucratic controls. Shenkin and Warner prefer instead decentralized regulation so far as it is necessary:

> [Therefore,] self-regulating, decentralized peer review would provide better individual assessments than centralized review [which

is all that is available now], since reviewers could correlate the patient himself with the record, instead of merely checking its internal consistency. [These improvements] would all take place without an increase in bureaucracy, as patients were enfranchised by decentralization instead of partially disenfranchised by centralization (p. 691).

Shenkin and Warner are aware of a number of objections that will be made to their proposal, and they try to deal with them. For example, they know that in all record keeping there is some tendency for form to prevail over substance and that this tendency might be enhanced when the physician knew that the patient could see it and have it checked easily. To protect themselves, physicians might do too much, enter too much into the record; they "might be less free to practice in the most expeditious way possible, and the record might become a real burden." Again, instead of making quality review by physicians the expected norm, available records might rally fearful physicians more into supporting one another's shortcomings than into correcting them. Shenkin and Warner feel that "much of the unwarranted fear of review would be assuaged with experience." Moreover, they think that this kind of "decentralized review with voluntary sanctions might be easier to accept than centralized alternatives" such as now seen threatened by such governmentally mandated organizational methods as professional standards review organizations. As to objections to the increased time required to write a good record for the scrutiny of the patient and one's peers, they think this would be "productive time" that would improve "the quality of clinical decision making both at the moment and in the future." They also feel that better education of patients would correct any great tendency of patients to misuse their records by treating or mistreating themselves. In sum, they see the benefits of their proposals as greatly outweighing any expected disadvantages.

The response of the medical profession to this radical and optimistic proposal for altering doctor–patient communication process has not been positive, as might have been predicted. As one letter writer to the *Journal* pointed out, the right of the patient to see and have his medical record has not even been included in the new Patients' Bill of Rights of the American Hospital Association. Other correspondents pointed to some realistic difficulties, such as the presence in the medical record of confidential information provided by the spouse, which the patient should not see. There are also problems when the diseases treated are venereal, psychosomatic, or terminal. Having confronted this response, Shenkin and Warner nevertheless feel that all questions about the benefits they foresee and the disadvantages others warn against could "be tested experimentally." Basically, they remain in agreement with Professor George Annas, one of the letter writers and a legal specialist in medical ethics at Boston University, who said: "The purpose of changing the system should be primarily to recognize patient rights and improve the quality of patient care. To this end, efforts should be made to standardize record forms and explain them to patients. All will be better served if the medical profession takes the lead in implementing this patient right." Effective communication and informed consent in medical systems are central to the improvement of the relationships in those systems. (For a further discussion of the pros and cons of patient access to medical records, with recommendations for a program that seeks to balance the patient's and the doctor's needs, see Westin, 1977. One of our longtime and distinguished students of the problem of privacy, Westin sets his discussion of patient access to medical records in this larger value context.)

COMMUNICATION AND CONSENT IN MEDICAL RESEARCH

Thus far we have dealt primarily with the problems of communication in medical therapy, not research. These problems in the therapeutic situation are important in themselves; new forms of informed consent are being demanded by patients in treatment. But they also shed much light on informed consent in medical research. The two situations often coexist; the presence of the physician in both is of primary importance in determining procedures and outcomes, and the patient often does not distinguish between the two. Nevertheless, the research situation has come to have some distinctive features, to be hedged about by new social controls; and it is therefore necessary to study it in its own right.

The Old Pattern and the New

Under the older pattern for dealing with subjects in medical research, there was little if any communication about the risks and benefits of research, no informal or formal requirement of informed consent, and an assumption that the medical researcher had the right, in the name of science of course, to do what he wished with the subject. A vivid picture of the older pattern has been sketched by a clinical investigator whose career started in the earlier period and extends into the present:

> Some years ago, when I was a research fellow, I had the job of finding suitable patient subjects for renal physiologic studies. In my first encounter with a suitable subject, a man who had recently recovered from pneumococcal pneumonia, I indicated to him that I wanted to study his kidney function if he didn't mind. I explained what the study would entail and told him that the data derived might be interesting and even important. He asked whether he had a kidney problem. I replied that he did not. He asked why he needed the kidney test. I replied that he really didn't, but . . . "Wait a minute," he said. "I didn't come to this hospital to be anybody's guinea pig; I came here to get well." I told one of my mentors that I had been unable to secure a study subject and explained what had happened. He responded, "You didn't do it right. You don't ask a patient if he minds being studied; you tell him that on a certain day you are going to study his kidneys. Remember, patients can always refuse." With this approach, no patient refused a scheduled test of his kidney function (Morris, 1972, p. 783).

> This approach was probably typical of that of many clinical investigators in university hospitals who needed human subjects for studies on a problem either unrelated to a patient's primary illness or a problem related to the illness but whose solution would be of not predictable benefit to the patient. I believe that many investigators allowed patients to infer that studies not predictably in the patient's best interest were part of the patient's optimal total medical evalution (p. 784).

Even worse than this "dissimulation," in many research-oriented charity hospitals "it was considered not unreasonable to do clinical investigation on charity patients with little explanation of the procedure and not even the pretense that the study was part of a complete medical evalaution." (See Barber et al., 1973, Chap. 3, for systematic evidence on worse treatment of ward patients in research.)

In addition to what this investigator calls "the sense of preemptory right" of researchers not to request informed consent from subjects, researchers also kept them in ignorance and deceived them; they were afraid that if they informed the subjects they would not participate, as in the case of the patient described above. There was no good evidence that this fear was justified, but it prevailed despite at least some evidence to the contrary. For example, beginning in the late 1950s, Park and his colleagues undertook studies at the Phipps Clinic at Johns Hopkins, demonstrating that informed subjects did not refuse their consent (Park et al., 1966; Park, Covi, and Uhlenhuth, 1967). These researchers concluded that

> 1) the welfare of the patient and the doctor–patient rapport will be better protected in the long run if it is a matter of routine to inform the patient of key aspects of the research, 2) the patient's preconceived notions and prior experiences determine his expectations to a degree that they are not easily shaken by whatever information is given to him, 3) patients will be likely to accept unusual or even unpleasant research procedures when they are explained with care in the setting of a good doctor–patient relationship, and 4) informed consent does not limit studies and actually can be a valuable asset to research design (Park et al., 1966 p. 200).

Since the promulgation in 1966 of the National Institutes' new rules for informed consent which apply to all research funded by it, procedures and practice for communication to the subjects of medical research have improved considerably. According to these new rules, as stated in a revised version:

> The basic elements of informed consent are:
> 1. A fair explanation of the procedures to be followed, including an identification of those which are experimental;
> 2. A description of attendant discomforts and risks;
> 3. A description of benefits to be expected;
> 4. A disclosure of appropriate alternative procedures that would be advantageous for the subject;
> 5. An offer to answer any inquiries concerning the procedures;
> 6. An instruction that the subject is free to withdraw his consent and to discontinue participation in the project or activity at any time.

In addition, the agreement, written or oral, entered into by the subject, should include no exculpatory language through which the subject is made to waive, or appear to waive, any of his legal rights, or to release the institution or any of its agents from liability for negligence (1971, p. 8).

Nonetheless, despite these improved procedures for communicating with research subjects, and despite the probable improvement in actual practices, a variety of research evidence indicates that problems remain. The research subject is still the victim of misunderstanding, of undue pressure, and of evasions. (For a report of an observational study of evasions used in getting informed consent forms signed in a psychiatric hospital, see Lidz, 1977.) For example, despite the explicit statement of the DHEW rules that for all research procedures there must be "an identification of those which are experimental," there is widespread unwillingness in the medical research community to use the term *experimental*. A variety of evasive terms such as *study* and *test* are used instead.

In 1973, testifying before the Senate Subcommittee on Health under the chairmanship of Senator Kennedy, Dr. Robert Veatch of the Hastings Institute reported that he had collected a file of forty-three "questionable experiments," all published "in reputable medical journals or presented at major professional meetings since 1966." While there were a variety of defects in these studies, many involved poor communication with the subjects. "The tragic fact," Veatch said, "is that less than 25 per cent of the studies in our file claim that consent was obtained from the participating subjects in the research, and not one paper documented the nature of the information given to subjects in conjunction with their consent." In reply to a question from Senator Kennedy, Dr. Veatch also stated it as his view that "the clinic population," the poorer, less educated population, was "the major contributor of research subjects" (U.S. Senate, 1973, p. 1123).

On a later occasion, in a paper prepared for the National Commission for the Protection of the Human Subjects of Biomedical and Behavioral Research, Veatch expressed a more generalized and systematic dissatisfaction with the present six elements of informed consent given in the DHEW regulations. There are, he says, some additional elements I believe a reasonable person would want to know before giving an adequately informed consent. These include:

1. A specific disclosure of the presence of a control group within the research design.
2. A statement of the inconveniences as well as the risks and discomforts.
3. Names of review and patient protection agents including the person in the institution and the person at the federal level who should be contacted if the subject has further questions about the experiment.
4. A statement of the basic rights of the subject. This should include not only the presently required statement of the right to withdraw without prejudice, but the right to access to the alternative treatments, mention of which is now presently required.
5. Explanation of who, if anyone, will be responsible for harms done to the subject. This should include an explanation of who, if anyone, will be responsible for both anticipated harms the risk of which was included in the consent, and negligent and non-negligent, but unanticipated harms.
6. An explanation of the right, if any, to continue receiving treatment found helpful to patient/subject (Veatch, 1978, p. 30).

(For another statement of additional elements, see Levine, 1978b. This is a useful detailing and specification of what all the elements mean in practice.)

In 1974, Smith reported on a study he made in 1970–1971 of a group of twenty-three patients participating in a study of myocardial infarction in a hospital's cardiac care unit. This was a study of the risky procedure of cardiac catheterization, a procedure involving "placement of an arterial and central venous silastic catheter, which would be positioned into the coronary sinus via a superficial neck or arm vein. Body temperature, arterial and venous pressures, and electrocardiogram were to be continually monitored, certain biochemicals were to be measured in serial samples of arterial and coronary sinus blood, coronary blood flow would be estimated, and cardiac output would be calculated" (Smith, 1974, p. 399). Smith made tape recordings of the consent requests by the doctors, he had follow-up interviews seventy-two hours later with the subjects, and he had conversations with attending medical and nursing staff. In ten of the recorded consent-request interactions, "there was no mention at all of risks associated with the procedure. In two conversations risk was acknowledged in response to direct questions, in one case from the patient himself and in the other from the patient's wife" (p. 400). Even in those interactions where consent was requested, however, "patients were reassured that the procedure was 'routine.' " Smith reports the following comments as typical: "Pretty much routinely now, we're taking people with infarcts and putting in a catheter"; "Routinely on them now, we're putting a small catheter into the right atrium"; "There are no real risk factors involved"; "It's attended by extremely little risk"; and, "They're getting to be more or less routine tests that we're doing." In sum, says Smith, "in none of the 23 cases studied, however, were possible complications or risks specifically described to patients" (p. 401). This is evasion of communication responsibilities by omission. How did the patients feel about this unsatisfactory communication? In his interviews with them seventy-two hours after admission, Smith discovered that although twelve of the patients felt "reasonably comfortable with the information they had received," another ten "felt that the procedure was not fully explained and that they did not know altogether what was being done to them" (p. 402). (One patient was unable to communicate with Smith.) In his study of the tape recordings of the consent-request situation, Smith discerned four "varieties of physician–patient relationship." These "ranged along a spectrum from (a) harassment and belligerence, to (b) subtle economic coercion, to (c) confusion and manipulation, to (d) helpful and supportive alliance." The first three, he says, "are encroachments on the trust and confidence which ordinarily obtains in the physician-patient relationship." That the patients somehow reacted to this encroachment is perhaps indicated by the fact that "a majority" of the patients who finally consented told Smith that "they would not consent to a second catheterization procedure." The patients had not consented because they had been satisfactorily told about risks and benefits and alternatives, as the DHEW regulations require. Rather, "their real motivation lay in fear and a willingness to do anything that had even the appearance of contributing to their recovery" (p. 403). Smith concludes that in the case of myocardial infarct patients, who are suffering from shock and fear in what is defined as an emergency situation, it would be better not to try to obtain informed consent from them but either get it from "appropriate next of kin" instead or abandon it altogether and permit physicians to operate under "the 'reasonable care' doctrine." The former may be a suitable alternative, but the latter seems to be a retrogression from the new moral standards prescribed for satisfactory communication with the patient-subject. Indeed, in this case communication was established with nearly all the patients. If the doctors had been better trained or had so wished, they could have communicated better with even these distressed patients.

Further evidence on the inadequacy of communication in the research situation as it is actually experienced by subjects themselves is provided by careful research carried out by Dr. Bradford Gray in the early 1970s (Gray, 1975a). With the consent of the principal investigator at a distinguished university hospital and research center, Gray interviewed fifty-one women who had been the subjects of research on the labor-inducing effects of a new drug. All of these women had actually signed consent forms, but often in the hectic course of the admitting procedure or even in the labor room itself—and then too often as administered by a harried nurse rather than the physician-researcher or one of his junior medical assistants. It turned out that twenty of the subjects (39 percent) learned only from Gray's interviews that they were the subjects of research. Note that Gray's interviews occurred after the drug infusion had commenced or, in some cases, even after delivery. Moreover, even among those who did know that they were in a research study, most did not understand at least one important aspect of the study: that there might be hazards; that it was a double-blind experiment; that they would be subject to special monitoring and subsequent test procedures; that they were not required to participate; or that there were effective alternatives. Four of the women said they would have refused to participate if they had known they had a choice. Some of the women were ward or clinic patients, but many had been referred for the study by their private physician, who had informed them not that an "experimental" drug was to be administered but only that a "new" drug was to be used. They trusted their doctors and assumed that this conventional evasion, this use of "new," meant better. Gray's study gives hard evidence on some continuing problems with communication in the medical research situation.

Another study asking the question, "Are Research Subjects Really Informed?" is presented in a report by Schultz and Pardee, a physician and a nurse (1975). These investigators interviewed a random sample of fifty new patients admitted in 1972 to the Clinical Research Center of the University of Washington Hospital in Seattle. These subjects were participating in twenty-three of the hundred research projects then going on at the center. Within an hour or two of their consent interviews, the patient-subjects were approached; and the purpose of the study—to study informed consent—was explained. They were then asked a series of questions to see to what extent their experience of the admission consent interview complied with the criteria for informed consent stipulated in the DHEW guidelines. In the light of these criteria, 48 percent of the subjects were judged to be inadequately informed. The findings showed that "patients were best informed about costs [of hospital care] and least well informed about benefits and risks. Such crucial items as procedures, purposes, risks and freedom to withdraw were understood only by about 25 percent of patients" (p. 76). Information about costs was so good because "many had learned from other sources that they would bear no costs of the research stay in hospital or any complications thereof" (p. 77). Although each patient was supposed to receive a copy of his signed consent forms, only ten patients had in fact received one. The space on the form for the name of a witness was "frequently" left blank. When seven independent judges were asked to rate consent forms for ease or difficulty of comprehension, 37 percent of the seventy judgments indicated that the forms were difficult to understand, many of the statements being long and complex.

This study confirms that written consent, unaccompanied by satisfactory oral communication, often does not result in real informed consent. These investigators recommend that

> The consent form should be presented at the beginning of the
> process, when research admission to the hospital is first pro-
> posed to the patient. It should be left with him to read, consider,
> and discuss with anyone he chooses. After a suitable time inter-
> val, *before* he is admitted to hospital, he should be encouraged,
> in the presence of a witness who has no involvement in the study,

to ask questions, and only when both are satisfied, to sign.
(Schultz and Pardee, 1975, p. 80).

McCollum and Schwartz in fact found that understanding was
better when the research protocol had been reviewed by
mothers prior to the actual admission of their children to a research ward (1969). They also feel that "nonmedical editors"
would be valuable for reviewing the final wording of all consent
forms.

Finally, research data on the persisting inadequacies of communication in informed consent procedures can be found in a
national sample survey study carried out, under the auspices of
the National Commission for the Protection of Human Subjects,
under the direction of Drs. Arnold Tannenbaum and Robert
Cooke at the University of Michigan Survey Research Center
(Cooke, Tannenbaum, and Gray, 1978). This study included
sixty-one research institutions and inquired into their performance on ethical requirements during the period from July 1,
1974 to June 30, 1975. It was found that between one-third and
one-half of the research proposals eventually approved by the
peer review committees of these institutions had been modified
in some way during the formal review process. Moreover, informed consent procedures were a considerable part of the corrective activity by the committees. In 24 percent of the projects
they screened, they required changes in the procedures for obtaining consent from subjects. Because of their concern for this
problem, 96 percent of the committees required that investigators submit consent forms for review. The survey also found
a trend away from standard consent forms for any and all
studies toward forms written specifically for each new study.
Some faults in consent forms remain, however. Committees
rarely required that the consent forms for studies designed
primarily to benefit subjects describe the alternative possibilities
for treatment. And certain conventional evasions persist. In 60
percent of the experimental studies, there was no explicit identification of the work as experimental through the use of such
words as *experiment, research,* or even *investigation.* In their
content as well, the consent forms were found to have defects.
Tannenbaum and Cooke used the standard Flesch technique
for evaluating the readability of consent forms and generally
found them hard to read. Few forms provided lay explanations
of medical and technical terms, though this was not their main
defect. The sheer complexity of the sentence structure and the

excessive length of the words used were what made them hard to read. (An interesting discussion of the applicability of readability research to the information contents of the package inserts in various drugs can be found in Pyrczak, 1978. Such research, in the case of estrogens for use in the relief of menopausal symptoms, shows the difficulties patients have in reading the present package inserts.)

SUGGESTED IMPROVEMENTS IN CONSENT PROCEDURES

Given the awareness and evidence that communication remains defective in informed consent procedures, it is not surprising that there should be suggestions for its improvement. It is to be expected that the methods for obtaining satisfactory informed consent, like all relatively new social technologies, will undergo a series of incremental improvements, as "bugs" in the methods are recognized.

A considerable improvement in these procedures would probably result if medical researchers treated the consent problem as seriously as they treat the methodological and theoretical parts of their research. To many researchers, the consent–request situation and the consent form are still formalities required by an alien outsider, the government, not an important cognitive and moral enterprise. (For an observational study of the hostility of medical researchers to informed consent procedures, see Lidz, 1977.) If it were so redefined, if medical researchers talked with themselves, so to speak, before they talked with subjects or made up consent forms, the outcomes might be much better. As George Herbert Mead has taught us, we are all social creatures who are human because we participate in what he called "the generalized other," that constellation of knowledge and norms we have internalized that makes our membership in society and social relationships possible. A conversation with oneself in regard to the consent situation is a kind of conversation with others, an anticipation of what they might cognitively understand and define as moral. In considering what to say to a subject, either orally or through the consent form, the doctor will find it helpful first to rehearse the conversation seriously with himself or, in a situation of change, with respected colleagues as well. Writing a consent form and explaining it to the subjects could become a normatively and cognitively instructive process for the researcher, instead of a resented formality that is delegated to others and to standard forms.

Going beyond this kind of serious conversation with self and colleagues, other improvements for informed consent procedures have been suggested. Fost has suggested that once consent statements have been composed, they be "tried out" on "surrogate" patients, that is, "individuals who in fact are not candidates for investigative or therapeutic procedures, but who are asked to behave as if they were" (1975, p. 800). Fost feels that such surrogates can "feel free to question any aspect of the procedure, free of the sense of dependency that may lead 'real' patients to go along with almost anything." To test the feasibility of his assumption, Fost conducted a pilot study on a sample of sixteen parents randomly selected from a private pediatric practice. Each of these surrogates was a woman who had recently given birth to a normal child. They were asked to "pretend" that their children had been premature and that they were being asked to include the infants in a controlled study of the effectiveness and hazards of umbilical artery catheterization. "The mother was then given a candid account of the reasons for the study and a full description of all known hazards of the procedure, as based on recent publications" (p. 801).

The parents seemed to find this hypothetical situation real enough to respond with either consent or refusal and with critical comment. One mother gave her unequivocal consent; seven were ambivalent but leaned toward consent; two refused outright; and two were ambivalent but leaned toward refusal. Fost remarks first that the "desire of four of the subjects not to participate in the hypothetical study is of interest in that consent is not generally sought for this widely practiced procedure." In addition, there was a "diversity of comments, criticisms, and suggestions" from the mothers. Some said they would refuse because the research was not really for the benefit of their infants. Others expressed a desire to consult with someone other than the doctor doing the research—another trusted doctor, a relative, a clergyman, or a psychologist. "A few mothers interviewed had sufficient medical knowledge to make substantial comments about the scientific rationale for the procedure, or to suggest alternatives." In sum, Fost concludes, "this pilot project suggests that a 'surrogate' model can be useful in uncovering attitudes toward a specific research protocol. The responses seemed more candid and diverse than those usually heard in actual clinical settings. . . . A surrogate system might provide one means of determining what a reasonable person might or might not consent to" (p. 803). The responses of Fost's subjects indicate that patients "would feel more free to ask questions and reflect on their decisions if the request for consent came from a different source, or if at least they had the opportunity to consult with an outside source" (p. 803). Some may ask if the hypothetical situations presented to "surrogates" are "real." Surely they are not identical with a clinical situation where the subject is actually facing a medical problem, but nonetheless they are "real" enough to elicit the kinds of useful information that would help a researcher in improving his consent procedures and consent forms. This "surrogate" technique is well worth further exploration of the kind Fost had given it.

We have several times earlier seen that the difficulty, length, technicality, and complexity of the consent form are hindrances to effective communication with the research subject. A carefully controlled study of some of these problems by Epstein and Lasagna provides a number of useful suggestions for change in the content of the consent form (1969). Sixty-six hospital employees, including secretaries, technicians, social workers, and nurses, but excluding doctors and medical students, volunteered for a study and were randomly assigned to three different groups, each of which was given a different consent form for a study that they were told "was designed to evaluate the effectiveness of an established remedy in relieving headaches." Those who participated would be asked to take two tablets of either "acetylhydroxybenzoate" (a fictitious name) or a placebo, a sugar pill. The participants in the three different groups were given information forms similar in regard to the main points about the purpose of the study, the dose of the drug, and the duration of the study, but differing in regard to length and the amount of descriptive material about the test drug. One form was succinct and only one page in length; another had the same basic information but was more detailed in all respects; and the third went to even greater lengths in describing actions, side effects, and possible toxicity. It should be disclosed here that all the information in the three forms about "acetylhydroxybenzoate" was taken from the section on aspirin in a standard textbook of pharmacology. After reading the different forms, participants were asked whether they were willing to become subjects and why. They were also given a questionnaire testing their knowledge of the basic information contained in the forms on the essential matters of purpose, design, indications, side effects, and risk. Finally, they were asked to evaluate the statement for clarity and length.

The findings showed significant differences among those receiving the short, medium, and long forms. "The group receiving the short form demonstrated the best comprehension," the medium-form group performed next best, and the long-form group the worst. Epstein and Lasagna feel that "in many cases, the detailed descriptions of the side effects or toxic actions apparently served to frighten the subject." Many subjects said that the detailed descriptions were frightening or confusing or both and that it would have been better simply to say that large overdoses might be fatal than to give a detailed account of salicylate intoxication. Length in itself does not necessarily convey essential material to subjects. Epstein and Lasagna rightly conclude that substance is more important than form, that succinct but relevant statements can be more effective than lengthy, needlessly detailed, and technical statements that frighten or confuse rather than convey the essential information needed for informed consent.

It can be seen from the Epstein and Lasagna study and from others we have described that asking the prospective subject what and how much he understands after reading the consent form is a useful device for improving communication and consent. It has been proposed by Miller and Willner that this arrangement be institutionalized for all consent procedures through the use of what they call "the two-part consent form" (1974). The first part, they say, "would be the current consent form—a statement of purposes, procedures, risks, discomforts, alternatives, and rights. The second would be a short list of questions about the information contained in the first part, and its purpose would be to check how well the subject understood the information expressed there" (p. 966). They suggest questions to cover knowledge of "six basic categories of information." On benefits, for example, to see how realistic the subjects' expectations are, they suggest a question, "Do you expect this experiment to benefit you directly in any way? If so, in what ways?" On the matter of the subjects' awareness of alternative treatments, they suggest the question might be, "Are you giving up customary treatment for the period of this experiment?" or "What alternative methods of treatment are available to you?" To check on knowledge of risks, the question might be, "Are there any dangers to you from being involved in this experiment? If so, what are they?" On the matter of understanding specific details of the experimental procedure, questions will vary from experiment to experiment, but an example might be, "How long will the needle remain in your arm?" And finally, to determine whether subjects know that they need not participate, the question could be, "What will happen if you decide not to participate or if you later decide to withdraw from the experiment?" (p. 966).

It is obvious that such a two-part consent form would greatly improve communication and consent. Miller and Willner suggest that someone other than the investigator judge whether the answers to the second part of the form indicate satisfactory knowledge on the part of the subjects. Where the answers are satisfactory, willingness to participate would definitely be based on informed consent. Where they are not, a further effort to explain and clarify might be made. If many subjects gave unsatisfactory answers, the first part of the form could be revised accordingly. If the subject could not understand after a couple of tries, it would be better not to ask him to participate. "We appreciate the costs in time, money, and effort that implementing our proposal would entail," say Miller and Willner, "but we believe that its goals are well worth the costs. Furthermore, the addition of the second part . . . would help demonstrate that scientists and investigators are genuinely concerned that the human subjects of their investigations voluntarily and understandingly participate" (p. 967). Medical researchers have a new ethical obligation to spend a little less time, if necessary, on the science part of their research activities, a little more time on working to get better communication with their subjects in the interests of more satisfactory informed consent.

DECEPTION IN MEDICAL RESEARCH

We have now reviewed a variety of forms of unsatisfactory communication processes in informed consent procedures, such as misunderstandings, different vocabularies of health and illness, omissions, and evasions. Apart from these inadequacies, a further question is often asked by laymen: is there any deception in medical research? Because *deception* can have a variety of meanings, the answer to this question cannot be simple. If by deception one means any evasion or omission or less than full disclosure, the answer, as we have seen in much evidence from studies, has to be yes. If, however, one means clever and deliberate obfuscation or lies, then the answer is no. One of the reasons for moral outrage against many psychological experiments is that deception in this latter sense does occur. (There is a whole literature discussing deception in the psychological journals, especially *The American Psychologist,* the journal of the American Psychological Association specifically concerned with professional problems. One article surveyed one thousand studies published in the journals of the American Psychological Association and reported on the amount and kinds of deception found in them. See Menges, 1973. For two carefully reasoned statements, one pro the other con, on deception in psychological research, see Berkowitz, 1978, and Baumrind, 1978. Both papers were commissioned by the National Commission for the Protection of Human Subjects.) For example, when electrodes are strapped onto subjects in psychological experiments, even though no physiological measurements are actually to be taken, a kind of lie is being perpetrated that seems to come more out of a tradition of "clever" and manipulative research than out of any inherent need of successful experimentation. Instances of this kind of deception, of deliberate lying or obfuscation, seldom occur in medical research. One such case occurred when patients were told they had been given chest operations although the operations had never been performed.

One research practice where generalized deception might be charged against medical research occurs when randomized controlled trials (RCTs) are used to conduct tests of the effectiveness of new or old drugs, operations, procedures, or regimens. (Fried, 1974, especially Chaps. 3 and 6, argues vehemently against RCTs, primarily on grounds of unfairness; but the deception issue is also important to him.) Randomized controlled trials are a powerful methodology, increasingly used, for establishing the effectiveness of medical treatments; they have been used for many different drugs and for such surgical procedures as coronary bypass operations. In randomized controlled trials, one randomly selected group is given the test agent, the other randomly selected group is given the inactive agent—the placebo, as it is commonly called. Neither group is supposed to know which agent is being given. Indeed, when RCTs are made "double blind," even medical personnel do not know which of the two agents they are giving to the patient. Double-blind procedures are possible, of course, only for some kinds of treatments such as drug therapy, and not for surgical procedures.

Does all this necessarily involve deception? Again, it depends on what the term is taken to mean. If all patients are asked to consent to a study which they are told is to be an RCT and told that their chances are only one out of two of getting the active agent or one of the two possible medical procedures or treatments, then no lie is involved and therefore no deception in that sense. Deception in this sense would occur only if the patients were not told that such an RCT was being done and were being used as subjects without their informed consent. This case reminds us again that communication is not an absolute in medical relationships. Not everything called *deception* by anyone is to be defined, morally or legally, as deception. RCTs are too valuable a methodology to be abandoned in the face of an ill-defined charge of deception.

6

Socialization, Social Control, and Informed Consent

In the earlier chapters, we have seen how a variety of moral and legal values, norms, and rules, on the one hand, and a variety of authority and communication roles, on the other, affect the principles and practice of informed consent in medical therapy and research. Since the values, norms, and roles that make up social relationships and social systems are not innate to human beings, they have to be learned in what is often a lifelong process. Moreover, since learning is usually far from perfect, since there are always a number of pressures to nonconformity in social systems (such as competing norms or competition between norm-obligations and role-pressures), and finally, since the endless changes that occur in social systems always require the learning of some new norms and roles, there have to be mechanisms of maintaining conformity, checking deviance, and helping people to cope with change. Learning about values, norms, and roles we call education or socialization—the induction of the novice into his social system. We all have to be socialized into satisfactory performance in our society. Doctors have to be socialized into all the rules and roles

122

of their special social system, including the rules and roles that affect informed consent. Similarly, as we all have to be subject to a variety of forms of social control in our society, so physicians have to acquire the set of special social controls necessary for proper behavior in medical relationships, again *including those having to do with informed consent.* In this chapter, we shall examine the structures, processes, and outcomes of the socialization and social control mechanisms that determine in part how physicians behave with regard to informed consent for their patients and subjects.

A word of caution is needed about the term *social control.* Given the great value the medical profession puts on individualism and autonomy, any term including the word *control* is likely to be suspect and despised. As we use it, however, *social control* is a generic analytic term for describing a variety of social structures and processes necessary to produce a certain kind of social performance. Each type of social control process can be, and often is, evaluated as well as described; but that is another matter. Certainly, social control is not necessarily dictatorial. The most democratic social systems need social control mechanisms, which will be different from those evaluated as dictatorial. Indeed, even within democratic social systems there will be small but important differences among the different varieties of possible social control structures. In those societies that strive to be democratic the task of keeping social control structures both effective and as egalitarian as possible is difficult and endless. This is certainly the case for the social control mechanisms having to do with informed consent in medical relationships.

Though socialization structures and social control structures are analytically separable from one another, they are in fact always interwoven, and they operate concurrently. We start with socialization and informed consent only for purposes of tidy exposition.

MEDICAL STUDENTS AND INFORMED CONSENT

In 1969–1970, seeking to learn how aware physicians were of the problem of informed consent in research and how their concern or the lack of it might have been molded by their medical education, my colleagues and I carried out the first large-scale and systematic research into these matters (Barber et al., 1973; Lally, 1978). Our group conducted two studies, one a mail survey of a nationally representative sample of three hundred institutions doing biomedical research using human subjects, the second an intensive interview study with some three hundred fifty research physicians in two institutions—the first called University Hospital and Research Center, the other Community and Teaching Hospital. These two studies collected data by asking the mail and interview respondents to report on their own experiences and behavior and to show their ethical concern for research subjects by evaluating detailed and technical research protocols in which the two key ethical issues of informed consent and risk–benefit ratio were involved. Our interest here is with the informed consent data and findings. As was also true on the risk–benefit ratio issue, we found a significant minority of respondents who were not much aware of the importance of obtaining informed consent from research subjects. For example, in their responses to one of our research protocols, a protocol describing research into the problem of chromosome break in users of hallucinogenic drugs, 23 percent of the respondents approved the protocol even though it did not specify that informed consent would be obtained and even though the subjects might have been in some danger of arrest if drug usage were disclosed.

Our data also showed that one of the sources of this defective concern for informed consent lay in the inadequacies of medical school education in this area. Of the three hundred researchers who responded to our mail survey, only 13 percent reported that they had been exposed in medical school to part of a course, a seminar, or even a single lecture on the ethical issues involved in experimentation with human subjects. In fact, 57 percent of the sample could not report a single learning experience in this area, whether from courses, informal contacts with professors, or conversations with fellow students. The figures were about the same for graduates of the so-called elite medical schools, of other United States schools, and of foreign schools.

Furthermore, our studies found that medical school education was defective in emphasizing scientific concerns at the expense of ethical concerns. For more than a half-century, we have lived in and profited mightily from the age of scientific medicine. The medical schools have transformed themselves into distinguished centers of scientific research and scientific medicine. Their faculties are increasingly selected for scientific stardom and their students for their talent and aptitude for scientific studies. The students thus selected have taken the star scientific performers among their teachers as their role-models and have themselves become either researchers and teachers in the enlarged system of medical schools or specialist practitioners. All this has been somewhat at the expense of the ethical concerns that ought to be another essential part of the experimental research that makes scientific medicine possible. When we asked the three hundred fifty researchers in our second study, many of whom are stars in their medical schools and powerful role-models for their students, to name a set of any three characteristics they valued in potential research collaborators, 86 percent mentioned "scientific ability," 45 percent mentioned "hard work," 43 percent mentioned "personality," but only 6 percent mentioned anything that could be classified as "ethical concern for research subjects." Science is clearly more important than such ethical concerns as informed consent. Without relinquishing the valuable emphasis on science, medical schools need to redress the present imbalance between scientific and ethical concerns.

Fortunately, since our data were collected in 1969–1970, efforts toward redressing the balance have been made. In a report on a survey of medical ethics teaching in medical schools carried out in 1974, Veatch and Sollitto (1976) describe the increased teaching of ethics, including problems of informed consent, in the 107 American medical schools. In contrast to the nearly total absence of such teaching as late as the 1960s, in the 1970s, as a result of the fact that informed consent and other ethical problems have been defined as social problems, some kind of course explicitly in medical ethics or in some related but overlapping area of interest now exists in nearly every American medical school. In addition, the schools have begun offering a variety of conferences, workshops, clinical case discussion series, and single lectures or lecture series. All of this activity *may be* a strong force for raising consciousness and increasing useful knowledge about informed consent principles and practices among medical students, younger investigators, and their older colleagues as well.

Unfortunately, the figures and facts in hand about this new activity are not so conclusive as we should like them to be with respect to its probable efficacy. There are questions about how strong a force for change it can be in medical schools dominated by scientific concerns. We have seen many other fads pass through the medical schools in recent years and leave a much smaller effect than their proponents hoped for. I refer to movements to persuade medical students to spend less time on "hard" subjects like biomedicine and more time on "soft" subjects like psychiatry, comprehensive care, community medicine, preventive medicine, and the like. Medical students, interns, and residents are bright, ambitious people who have no difficulty knowing what the prestigious, established, serious people on the faculty really take seriously. We need to know how many of the latter are taking medical research ethics and problems of informed consent seriously. We need to know how many such people are working on ethics courses with anything like the seriousness with which they engage in scientific research. Perhaps even more important, how many of the star members of the established faculty are treating ethical issues continuously and seriously in their discussions of basic scientific and clinical issues, where these ethical issues can perhaps best be treated? We note that in only six of the ninety-seven respondent schools in the Veatch and Sollitto survey where medical ethics is treated in some fashion are the ethics courses required. In forty-seven schools, the courses are elective, and we do not know how many students are enrolled. What we do know about medical students suggests that they take the required scientific and clinical courses seriously, and very little else (Carlton, 1978). We could be more certain that something important with regard to informed consent principles and practice was going on in medical teaching if we saw evidence that senior instructors were regularly and seriously talking about these matters in their everyday and routine activities: their classes, their rounds, their conferences; over lunch and in other informal meetings. There probably remains considerable room for improvement on what has recently occurred in medical school teaching about informed consent.

The difficulties of changing the attitudes of the science-oriented medical students are evident in a study reported by Coe, Pepper, and Mattis (1977). They did a longitudinal study at one medical school only, unfortunately, of the attitudes held by the successive entering classes of 1970 and 1971 both as freshmen and as seniors. The study shows that there was a certain admixture of a "new" type of medical student in the early 1970s, a more liberal and more socially concerned student who had been created by the student rebellions and other sociopolitical events of the late 1960s. This "new man" in medical schools seems to have been a very short-lived phenomenon, all but disappearing by the middle 1970s. Moreover, Coe, Pepper, and Mattis found that during medical school, even for the originally liberal students, there was a conservatizing trend. By the time of graduation, the attitudes of these students approached the conservative positions of their teachers and their predecessors. The authors conclude that the established processes of medical school socialization have not been much affected by recent curricular reforms or the handful of "new" type students. This conclusion would not be unsafe in regard to the new teaching about informed consent. Indeed, our most recent intensive study of the socialization of medical students reports, as one of its major findings, "the limited, almost nonexistent, socialization of medical students to ethical issues in clinical practice" (Carlton, 1978, p. xiii). This study finds that the whole emphasis of the present system of medical care and clinical teaching, at least in "Midwest University Hospital Center," is on the biomedical perspective, not on the patient as a "whole person," as a location for social and ethical problems as well as biological phenomena. Carlton speaks of "the futility of using the classroom" for teaching ethics when the everyday clinical situation of the hospital is characterized by "an absence of role models who act consistently within the norm of 'ethical concern.' Thus students learn to disregard questions of values" (1978, p. 4). All the institutional and ideological pressures of the clinical learning situation for the student teach him that "the good physician" takes for granted "the primacy of clinical judgment over moral choice."

INFORMED CONSENT IN INTERNSHIPS AND RESIDENCIES

Internships and residencies are essential postgraduate phases for the effective training of physicians for satisfactory performance in scientific medical and research careers. What do interns and residents learn about informed consent? The data from our interview study with the three hundred fifty physicians doing research at University Hospital and Research Center and at Community and Teaching Hospital give some answers to this question. Of those interviewed, 59 percent reported that they had been sensitized to such ethical issues of clinical research as informed consent and the risk–benefit ratio in *some new way* during internship or residency. In fact, 13 percent reported that such sensitization was their first awareness of these issues.

It is interesting to note that all the ethically socializing experiences reported by these researchers were informal, unintended, and ad hoc—not the result of formal courses or lectures. As "house officers" during internship and residency, these researchers had been responsible for the care of patients on wards and clinics; and they had become aware of the problems of informed consent when their senior and supervising professors wanted to use patients as research subjects or when they themselves administered experimental drugs or performed experimental procedures for their senior colleagues. These ward and clinic patients, without private physicians of their own, were also poorer and poorly educated, less able to protect their own interests and to demand the right of informed consent. It was not surprising that the data in our study showed that these ward and clinic patients were more likely not only to be used as research subjects but also to be used in those studies where the risk–benefit ratio was less favorable. The pressure of their senior researcher colleagues for suitable research subjects made these interns and residents aware of the ethical problems and turned them into somewhat ambivalent collaborators.

As Stephen Miller has reported in an extensive analysis of the internship program at the Harvard Medical Unit at Boston City Hospital, a distinguished research unit, the interns and residents identify potential subjects for the research interests of their senior colleagues. He says:

> The consulting physicians are interested in particular kinds of patients for their own reasons, either to further their knowledge or advance their research. Whatever they need patients for, it is almost impossible for them to keep watch for the kinds they need. Interns do this for them. . . . Interns obligate themselves to consulting physicians the first time they seek their help. In exchange for valuable information or services they must furnish the consults with information about patients who might be useful in clinical investigations (Miller, 1970, pp. 152–153).

While the intern is in principle free not to cooperate, in fact, says Miller, "I did not once see an intern refuse clinical investigators the permission to use his patients." This is why the problem of informed consent is more serious on the wards and clinics than in the private pavilions.

Carlton's study does not offer much evidence that things have changed, at least in university hospital centers, since the period studied by Miller. Her interns and residents were no less concerned for "clinical judgment" rather than "moral choice" than were the attendings. In fact, "Throughout the hospital," says Carlton, "informed consent is treated as a necessary evil, untenable in clinical practice, though it is necessary to go through the motions" (1978, p. 23). A great deal of patient care in hospitals is in the hands of residents and interns.

INFORMAL MECHANISMS OF SOCIAL CONTROL

We turn now to the mechanisms of social control that influence physicians' principles and behavior with regard to informed consent. When socialization is inadequate (as we have just seen that it is), or when pressures to nonconformity exist despite adequate learning of the rules (as they do among highly competitive medical research scientists), or when social changes cause changes in the established rules about informed consent (as we have seen changing values and legal rules are doing), then in all such circumstances social control mechanisms are necessary to forestall or correct the existing or likely deficiencies.

Informal mechanisms are the first line of defense against deficiencies. These are the mechanisms that occur in everyday, routine working relationships among colleagues or between doctors and patients. Sometimes by a word, sometimes in lengthier, more serious discussions, colleagues can set one another straight when they think they have violated some norms or are uncertain how to proceed in novel situations. Informal social control is usually casual, often unself-conscious, and especially effective among small sets of people who think of themselves as sharing a moral community. For physicians and researchers, their individualism makes this the preferred mode of social control. The other mode of social control consists of formal mechanisms, highly visible, organizationally or legally specified structures of rules, committees, and offices whose assigned task is to correct deficiencies in behavior or guide people in novel and uncertain situations. We shall shortly consider the institutional review board as a mechanism of formal social control dealing with principles and practice of informed consent in medical research centers.

Some data from the second of our two studies shed light on how informal social control processes actually occur among researchers with regard to informed consent. In this study, we collected a quantity of sociometric information about the attitudes and behavior of research colleagues toward one another. Biomedical research is now a highly collaborative enterprise, and we wanted to know how research collaborators interacted with regard to such ethical issues as informed consent. Our data showed that of the 424 research studies in which our respondents were engaged 81 percent involved two or more collaborators. What ethical influence do they have over one another?

Recall first the data we presented on preferred characteristics in research colleagues. Whereas 86 percent of the researchers mentioned "scientific ability" as desirable in a potential collaborator, only 6 percent mentioned "ethical concern for research subjects." This large salience of the value of science over the value of ethical concern was likely to have had some effect on the substance of social control processes among these researchers. More of their informal social control behavior would have to do with scientific standards and procedures than with ethical ones. Indeed, 32 percent of the respondents mentioned "intellectual honesty" as one of the desirable characteristics. Among the responses coded under this term were such judgments as the requirement that a collaborator must not distort data to fit his conceptions, an important scientific standard obviously.

We could make further inferences about social control processes among collaborators from other data we collected. For example, we could classify all our researchers as either "strict" or "permissive" on the basis of their responses to a research protocol that tested their willingness to engage in a risky bone marrow experiment. Our data showed that on the whole like tended to collaborate with like, that is, "strict" researchers collaborated with one another as did "permissive" researchers. This suggests ethically satisfactory informal social control processes among the "strict" and unsatisfactory ones among the "permissives." Fortunately, a kind of corrective informal control process seemed to be in operation. We asked our respondents to whom they had gone in the past year to discuss ethical questions arising in their own research. Our data indicated a tendency among investigators to discuss their ethical dilemmas with researchers whose ethical standards were different from their own. Researchers seem to be trying to insure that they are neither too strict (not so good a social control process?) nor too permissive (a better one?).

It is clear from all our data that informal social control processes for such ethical issues as informed consent are neither highly salient to medical researchers nor so effective as they might be in controlling delinquencies and coping with changing social expectations. This fact also emerges from Gray's study of informed consent procedures and outcomes in an experimental study using some fifty women to test the efficacy of a new drug for inducing labor in pregnancy (1975). Gray found that some 40 percent of the subjects were not properly informed and that many of them had been misled, all unself-consciously, by their obstetrician, a close colleague and friend of the research investigator to whom he recommended them as subjects. An excellent opportunity for favorable informal control processes by friendly colleagues, both generally ethical people, was missed because of their shared lack of knowledge and concern about the newly emerging higher standards for informed consent procedures.

Thus far we have reported data on the medical research situation. Deficiencies in informal control processes also occur in the therapeutic situation. Indeed, it may be in this prototypical encounter situation for doctors and patients that resistance even to informal control by medical peers and others—nurses, social workers, and other paramedicals—is strongest. Writing in a medical journal, an editorialist says:

> Most physicians have valued their integrity, have practiced well, kept up at least on the varieties of new discoveries and methods of treatment. However, the need to let this integrity be examined by those others with whom we spend our professional lives

produces a chill in more than one physician. . . . I've seen severe anxiety, over the prospect of opening up office records, in physicians whose training, experience, and certifications would almost certainly guarantee successfully passing almost any review. No quick answer can be given why this should be so (Headlee, 1972, p. 6).

Can this be a result of the intense value our present physicians have been trained to put on individualism and autonomy, a value so great that they are frightened even of the kind of moral and cognitive sharing with their colleagues essential in a world where science and other kinds of social change constantly bring about a need for adaptation through consultation and control by peers?

The *locus classicus* for research and analysis on the lack of effective informal social control among medical colleagues in the therapeutic situation can be found in the work of Eliot Freidson. Summing up more than twenty years of research and analysis, Freidson, in an article in the now-defunct popular journal, *PRISM*, which was sponsored by the American Medical Association, described the defective situation in this way:

The present practice environment is dominated by the need for the exclusive solidarity of the colleague group, which avoids mutual observation and correction. The individual's work, even in an organized group practice, is private. Nobody else may look to see how his colleague is performing. Discussions of error, even within the colleague group itself, are severely restricted. Concession of error is viewed as a severe threat to the individual and to the profession in general.

Such protective solidarity within the colleague group is also characterized by the permissive evaluation of colleagues when error does become known—justified by "There, but for the grace of God, go I," or, "It may be my turn next."

Finally, in the present environment of medical practice, a status system rigidly excludes outsiders from knowledge of and participation in activities within the colleague group. . . . Medical authority therefore governs everything related to the physician's work, including matters having no basis in technical medical knowledge or skill.

This holistic authority makes the physician the ultimate arbiter of others' work and of the acceptability of the patient's wishes. It also justifies the subordination of both allied health workers and patients and excludes them from participation in treatment (1974, p. 41; see also Freidson, 1970, especially pp. 93–103; 211–216, 223–237).

"It is not," says Freidson in the same article, "good manners to discuss a colleague's competence, even among colleagues. There is a conspiracy of silence about erring colleagues."

It is significant that the same phrase, "conspiracy of silence," was used by a California judge in rendering a decision in a malpractice case where it was abundantly clear not only that the defendant was highly incompetent but that his colleagues had multiply and consistently refused opportunities to correct and control him. (Editorial, "How Well Does Medicine Police Itself?" *Medical World News,* March 15, 1974.) In a 196-page memorandum of decision in this case, which involved a charge of negligent orthopedic surgery brought by a clerk against a Sacramento doctor, Judge B. Abbott Goldberg "told of at least 50 additional surgical procedures that may have been 'unnecessary, or bungled, or both.' He charged the physician with coercing patients to undergo surgery with threats, intimidation, and false-positive myelograms." The judge also "hinted that the medical community had attempted a cover-up of the case." For example, another doctor, a friend to the defendant and a neurosurgeon himself, could have exposed the malpractitioner on several occasions, according to Judge Goldberg. In addition, the hospital pathologist "failed to report" the defendant's incompetence, as revealed by his examination of surgically excised tissue, either to the chief of surgery or to the medical audit and tissue committee. Finally, "in addition to the handful of physicians who had direct knowledge" of the defendant's incompetence, "there were others, in Judge Goldberg's view, who might have blown the whistle. Throughout the memorandum, he names physicians who saw [the defendant's] patients for treatment after his operations." No wonder the judge echoed Freidson's phrase, "conspiracy of silence."

The system of informal control mechanisms essential to good technical and ethical practice in the therapeutic situation is badly in need of improvement. Proper principles and practice of informed consent suffer along with other aspects of satisfactory medical care.

Responding to a few similar scandalous cases of unreported

medical incompetence, New York State recently passed a law requiring its forty-four thousand licensed physicians to report instances of colleagues' professional misconduct (*Medical Tribune,* September 7, 1977). In case of demonstrable failure to do so, the witnessing physician is himself deemed guilty of misconduct and subject to disciplinary action. Other mandatory reporting statutes of this kind have already been enacted in Arizona, Alabama, Connecticut, Idaho, Iowa, Maine, Montana, Ohio, Oregon, and Virginia. To encourage physicians to report the incompetence or misconduct of their colleagues to the new Board for Professional Conduct, the New York statute grants them immunity from civil suit for such action.

New York State officials do not expect that this formal action to improve informal social control functions will have much effect on everyday practice. They estimate that only some 3 to 5 percent of physicians are grossly incompetent; and it is these they hope to have reported under the new law. They seek to eliminate "gross wilful negligence" rather than ordinary mistakes in judgment. Up to now, few physicians have helped in this task. The task force that prepared the report on which the New York State law was based found that only 79 out of 1191 complaints about doctors made to the Health Department's Office of Professional Medical Conduct came from persons other than aggrieved patients. Thirty-one came from doctors, thirty-seven from medical societies, four from hospitals, four from nurses, and three from insurance carriers. While seventy-four physicians have been disciplined as a result during the last three years by the New York State Board of Regents, which has final authority over the medical profession, not one physician had his license to practice revoked. We shall see, when we look at state licensing boards as one type of formal social control mechanism, that this pattern of mild discipline for medical incompetence is universal throughout the United States.

One final word about informal social control mechanisms in medical therapy and research. These mechanisms could probably be improved considerably not only by changes in the attitudes and behaviors of the physicians themselves but also by the inclusion of such paramedical professionals as nurses and social workers in the control processes. Because of the professional dominance of physicians, however, these other participants in medical care are fearful of entering complaints about technical incompetence and moral delinquencies such as bad informed consent practices.

As we have just seen, only four complaints about doctors in New York State came from nurses, who have excellent opportunities to observe deficiencies and whose own code of ethics requires them to protect the rights of patients. (On nurses, see Ellis, 1970; and Glaser and Strauss, 1965, pp. 188 ff.; on social workers, see Savard, 1970; and Adams, 1973.) That doctors are opposed to the inclusion of nurses and other medical professionals in informal social control processes is indicated by the statement of Dr. Don Harper Mills, a physician and legal expert on such matters as informed consent for the American Medical Association. Writing a reply to a comment on his article, "Whither Informed Consent?" in the *Journal of the American Medical Association,* Dr. Mills says, "Since most nurses are not competent to evaluate the propriety of disclosures required for informed consent, their presence as witnesses serves only to attest patients' signatures. This seems unduly wasteful" (230 [1974], 38). The inclusion of nurses and other associated professional medical workers in an informal social control team not only might not be wasteful but actually might improve the effectiveness of such teams.

FORMAL MECHANISMS OF SOCIAL CONTROL

Always there to complement the informal mechanisms of social control in medicine and other areas of social behavior are the formal mechanisms, the "bureaucratic" elements—explicitly designated, specially staffed, and legally defined to forestall and correct delinquency. Despite its great emphasis on individual autonomy and professional self-regulation, medicine has always found it necessary to have a variety of formal social control structures and procedures. State licensing boards, local county medical society ethics committees, tissue committees, and clinical pathological conferences for the staffs of hospitals—all are formal control mechanisms in some kind of existence for fifty years or more; but recent social changes have required the creation of still others. Most notable among these innovations are the institutional review boards for the ethical surveillance of the use of human subjects in biomedical research and the professional standards review boards for the surveillance of the effectiveness and economy of therapeutic procedures and practices in hospitals. All these structures and procedures have some important defects as social control mechanisms. In reviewing them, we shall start with the institutional review boards, which have been most directly concerned with the problem of informed consent. We are interested in the other formal mechanisms of social control in medicine, even though they are not always directly involved with procedures and practices governing informed consent, because they give us a better understanding of the general condition of professional self-regulation in medicine. The specific problems of informed consent have to be seen against the background of that general self-regulatory condition.

Institutional Review Boards

This generic term has come to be applied to local ethical peer review committees, now usually including some lay community members as well, that must approve every research protocol using human subjects. The two key issues the boards consider in every case, as we have seen already, are informed consent and the risk–benefit ratio for the research subjects.

As we might expect from the fact that informed consent has but recently become a social problem, the institutional review board mechanism designed to cope with this problem is a recent social invention. Indeed, it is best to consider it as an innovation still in the process of development. Its present form accomplishes a good deal, but much improvement is still needed. A brief history of the institutional review board will give us a better understanding of its progress to date and its persisting deficiencies.

As is also true of written codes of ethics for the use of human subjects, the first institutional review boards appeared in the 1950s and 1960s. Professor William J. Curran, a pioneer student of these matters, has said, "the need to identify and develop acceptable standards of care [for human subjects] began to receive limited but respectable support in the clinical research community in the late 1950's and early 1960's" (1969, p. 545). Fortunately, and quite unexpectedly, a small research project describes the state of affairs at that time quite well. In 1960, Dr. Louis Welt, a Yale Medical School physician, sent a questionnaire to every university department of medicine in the country asking them whether they had what he called "a procedural document dealing with problems of human experimentation" and whether they favored "a committee of disinterested faculty [to] review the experimental design to insure maximum protection for the subject" (1961, p. 75). Dr. Welt received replies from sixty-six of the eighty departments in existence at the time. He reported that only eight of his respondent institutions had a procedural document and only twenty-four had or favored having a review committee for human experimentation. Obviously, there was not much commitment to review committees. A few years later, the Law-Medicine Research Institute at Boston University, newly established by Professor Curran and colleagues, with a grant funded by the National Institutes of Health, undertook a study similar to Dr. Welt's (Curran, 1969). The results were similar: the institute survey of eighty-six departments produced fifty-two responses. Only nine departments had procedural documents, though five more said they were developing them or favored doing so. Twenty-two departments reported that they had peer review committees but that these were only "advisory." In sum, as Curran put it, "it is evident that in the medical research community prior to 1962 there was a general skepticism toward the development of ethical guidelines, codes, or sets of procedures concerning the conduct of research" (1969, p. 550). Furthermore, there was no outside pressure for change. "It was the posture of both the FDA and the NIH to allow and to encourage clinical investigators . . . to be guided by their own ethical standards as well as those of their institutions" (1969, p. 550).

Pressure for more numerous and more satisfactory institutional review boards in the medical schools finally came, partly as a result of public scandals and partly as a result of events occurring at the National Institutes of Health. In 1962, public horror was aroused by the news of the thalidomide tragedy in Germany, a disaster in which, as the result of the use of a new sedative drug during the pregnancies of their mothers, children were born with undeveloped arms and legs. This scandal stimulated the support necessary to pass the Drug Amendment Acts of 1962, acts which had been stalled in Congress since 1959.

One of the provisions of these Kefauver–Harris amendments was the first statutory regulation, through the Food and Drug Administration, of drug research using human subjects. At about the same time, another scandal, the Southam–Mandel case in New York, in which live cancer cells were injected into geriatric patients without their informed consent, further increased public concern with human experimentation. (Extensive documentation on the Southam–Mandel events can be found in Katz, ed., 1972.)

In 1966, as a result of these pressures and events, Commissioner Goddard of the F.D.A., after much consultation with the clinical drug research community, issued a detailed statement of policy concerning consent. This affected some, but not all, biomedical research using human subjects. An even more important occurrence of 1966 was the landmark action of the National Institutes of Health in issuing its procedural statement, "Protection of the Individual as a Research Subject." Because of its early concern for the human subjects of experimentation at its Clinical Research Center, the NIH had been working for some time on a policy for the ethical use of human subjects. The 1966 statement, requiring all NIH-funded research to be prescreened by a local institutional review board and laying down a detailed code of procedures and standards for such screening, was a watershed event in the formal control of biomedical research using human subjects. Because so much of American biomedical research is funded by the NIH, henceforth the institutional review board became almost universal. Moreover, institutions doing biomedical research have tended to include all research in the screening procedure, not just the part funded by the NIH. A successive series of regulatory statements by the NIH over the last dozen years has increasingly specified and improved the review board mechanism. One considerable change in the regulations has involved the use of outside or community members on the review boards. Whereas the use of such outside members was merely recommended in the 1966 regulations, the NIH has mandated their use in later statements.

The immediate widespread effect of the 1966 NIH regulations on the development of the institutional review board can be seen in some of the data collected by my colleagues and me in our study of a nationally representative sample of biomedical research institutions that had filed assurances with the NIH by

1969 that they had established such boards (Barber et al., 1973). Of our respondent institutions, 54 percent reported that they had complied immediately, in 1966; another 28 percent had done so in 1967; and the last 18 percent had done so in 1968 or 1969. Not only did the regulations bring new institutional review boards into existence, they also stimulated the improvement of boards that already existed. Almost two-thirds of the institutions that said they already had review boards in 1966 reported that they had made required or voluntary improvements in those boards as a result of the new regulations.

Not everything was immediately perfect, of course. Our data showed that only 86 percent of the respondent institutions reviewed *all* research; 9 percent still did not review research not contained in a formal proposal; and 4 percent said they reviewed only the research proposals submitted to NIH. Furthermore, as we discovered in our second study when we interviewed individual researchers at University Hospital and Research Center and Community and Teaching Hospital, even institutions that claimed to review all research did not in fact do so. Of the three hundred fifty researchers we interviewed at these two places, 9 percent *volunteered* that some of their research had not been reviewed, even though the institutions claimed they reviewed everything. Organizations do not work perfectly, and not everything one physician calls research is so defined by his peers.

We also found defects even where the institutional review boards were doing their jobs. Some review was not being conducted under the NIH-mandated conditions or what might be considered the most efficacious circumstances. For example, in many institutions there was, and there continues to be, a lack of the mandated *continuing* review. In some institutions, our data showed a lack of face-to-face discussion and moral consultation among peer reviewers. We also found an absence of clear and regularized appeal procedures for aggrieved researchers. This defect in the review process also continues to exist in most institutions. Finally, until recently, the institutional review boards have been nearly entirely isolated from one another. There was no forum, in the form of conferences, reporting journals, or journals of opinion, where they could learn from one another, consult on different cases, or in any way compare experiences as, say, courts of law do through their innumerable reviews, journals, and conferences. Fortunately, and probably for the improvement of IRB performance, a journal called *IRB: A Review of Human Subjects* commenced regular publication in March 1979. It is sponsored by the Hastings Center and is under the editorship of Dr. Robert J. Levine, professor of medicine at Yale and a longtime and knowledgeable participant in the field of biomedical ethics. He is assisted by an advisory board of experienced philosophers, lawyers, sociologists, scientists, and physicians. *IRB,* the first issue announces, "will be a forum for communicating information and ideas pertaining to the ethics of conducting research on [or involving] human subjects. [It hopes] to facilitate a better understanding of the ethics and regulation of research as well as the complexities of the review process. If successful, we will not only enhance our abilities to make more thoughtful decisions but also contribute to the efficiency of the review process" (p. 3).

How can we measure the actual effectiveness of institutional review boards in screening for unsatisfactory standards of informed consent in research protocols? My colleagues and I used a number of measures, but one—the rate of acceptance, revision, and rejection of proposals—will give us some rough sense of their efficacy as of the time of our research. In 31 percent of the respondent institutions, we were told, the review committees had required researchers to *revise* their proposals but had made *no rejections* at all; in 32 percent, committees had gone further and rejected one or more proposals outright; and in 3 percent there were no revisions and no rejections, but some cases of the withdrawal of proposals by investigators when they felt their research might be revised or rejected. In the remaining 34 percent, there had been no revisions, no rejections, and no withdrawals. Obviously, we may infer from this evidence that the committees were being effective in some degree. We could not interpret our evidence on the "inactive" committees, those with no revisions, rejections, or withdrawals. It could have meant that all proposals in these institutions in fact needed no improvement, or it could have meant that these committees were not effectively performing their duties.

Some research by Bradford Gray permits us to decide at least tentatively between these two possibilities (1975b). Gray's research had two parts, one a study of the extent to which subjects in an experiment to test the efficacy of a new drug for inducing labor had actually given informed consent, the second an investigation of the performance of the institutional review board at the distinguished medical and research institution where this test was carried out. Gray's committee was excellent, with a full commitment to the highest standard of efficacy in peer review. Two of its members were authorities on experimentation and informed consent and had published on this subject. Because of the committee's dedication, Gray was allowed to study the records on how it had actually reviewed seventy-nine research protocols (mostly surgery, internal medicine, and obstetrics and gynecology) for the academic year 1969–1970. Of these projects, only 28 percent were approved without modification by the committee. This is a low figure in comparison with the inactivity found in many of the boards in our study.

The issue most commonly raised by Gray's committee concerned informed consent. Most frequently, the committee found the consent forms to be incomplete; in some cases it found them inaccurate; and in still other cases it found inconsistencies between the description of research and what was said on the consent form about that research. The committee also found that the wording of the consent forms was not likely to be intelligible to the layman. In sum, says Gray, the records of this committee show it to have been "active, conscientious, and, with respect to most issues it addressed, effective. Its performance suggests both that review committees can have an impact on proposals and that there is need for such review" (1975b, p. 328). Furthermore, "the fact that the CRC found relatively few proposals which did not need some sort of modification also has implications for the interpretation of the Barber group's findings concerning the relative lack of activity by most review committees. Specifically, it appears that a record of few actions by committees is an indication that their members are indifferent or that their standards are loose, and that existing practices do not conform to present ethical standards" (1975b, p. 328). Gray's argument concerning the need for improvement in the procedures of institutional review boards seems plausible; and, of course, some improvement has occurred since his report was published.

Our most up-to-date evidence on the performance of the institutional review boards is provided in a study sponsored by the National Commission for the Protection of the Human Subjects of Biomedical and Behavioral Research and carried out by the Survey Research Center of the University of Michigan with the collaboration of Gray, at that time on the staff of the national commission (Cooke, Tannenbaum, and Gray, 1978; Gray, Cooke, and Tannenbaum, 1978). This research was carried out on a national sample of sixty-one research institutions. Interviews were conducted with more than two thousand investigators whose proposals had been reviewed by institutional review boards, with more than eight hundred members of such boards, and with more than one thousand research subjects. This study shows that on the whole the institutional review board continues to improve its efficacy but problems in its function remain.

Here are some of the study's specific findings. Review boards have become more active than they were at the time of our study. Researchers whose proposals had been reviewed reported that more than half the time they were not approved as first submitted. Sponsors of defective proposals were required to furnish more information and to make substantive changes as well. By far the most frequent substantive change concerned informed consent; changes in informed consent procedures or forms occurred in one-fourth of all proposals finally approved by the boards.

On the whole, researchers support the institutional review boards, but substantial minorities still oppose them on one or more grounds. Virtually all the investigators interviewed said the review procedure had protected the rights and welfare of subjects to some extent; two-thirds said that review had improved the quality of research; and almost all said that the procedure now runs with reasonable efficiency. Still, minorities ranging from one-quarter to one-half the researchers said they felt that ethical review is an unwarranted intrusion on their autonomy, that the review boards get into inappropriate areas, that they make judgments for which they are unqualified, and that the review process has impeded research. Despite this negativism, *fewer than ten percent* of the investigators were willing to go so far as to say that the difficulties and limitations of review outweigh its benefits for protecting human subjects and providing satisfactory informed consent. As Gray, Cooke, and Tannenbaum sum up, "Most researchers, as well as board members, apparently recognize a need for the review of research, accept the legitimacy of IRB's, and are prepared to play their part in supporting the work of these boards" (1978, p. 1100).

The study also found persisting defects in the institutional review boards' procedures and efficacy. First, although changes were frequently made in consent forms, with regard to their content and intelligibility, few changes were made in the way in which informed consent was to be obtained—that is, in the setting, timing, or personnel administering or witnessing the informed consent. Yet we know from Gray's earlier research and other studies that the way in which consent is obtained may be more important than any consent form or signature thereto (1975a; 1975b). The institutional review boards will have to pay more direct attention to actual informed consent interviews.

Second, even the consent forms themselves had defects. As measured by various objective indices of such matters, they were often low on readability. (For an interesting discussion of the applicability of readability research to the information contents of the patient package inserts in various drugs, see Pyrczak, 1978.) As measured on an index based on the six elements of disclosure required by the DHEW regulations, they were often incomplete. The forms sometimes did not mention the purpose of the research, the procedures involved, the benefits or lack of them for the subjects, the risk, and the fact that participation was voluntary and subjects could withdraw at any time, or provide an invitation to ask questions about participation. Fewer than one-fifth of the approved forms contained all these required elements of information. Though concerned about informed consent, the institutional review board does not show itself to be knowledgeable or very effective in this area.

Taking the evidence from the Cooke, Tannenbaum, and Gray study and the evidence and judgments presented at its hearings and discussions, the national commission has made a number of recommendations for the future of the institutional review board as a formal mechanism for the effective control of standards and practices with regard to informed consent and other issues in the protection of the human subjects of research (1978b). The commission accepts that the institutional review board is on the whole a satisfactory mechanism; it does not recommend fundamental changes. Indeed, because of its satisfaction with the IRB, the commission recommends that federal law be enacted to place all federal agencies themselves participating in or funding research using human subjects under the control of a single authority, the secretary of Health, Education, and Welfare. Going further still, the commission recommends that "all research involving human subjects sponsored or conducted by an institution that receives funds from any federal department or agency to provide health care or conduct health-related research" should be subject to federal regulation as administered by the secretary of HEW (1978b, p. 3). So important is such uniform regulation through institutional review boards that the commission recommends direct-cost funding of their activities, including payment for the administrative staffs and for time released from other duties for the chairmen of large and busy boards.

To carry out his regulatory function effectively, the commission recommends that the secretary of HEW establish a single office to accredit institutional review boards, to carry out monitoring and compliance functions such as site visits and audits, and to educate members of IRBs "in recognizing and considering the ethical issues that are presented by research involving human subjects" (1978b, p. 10). This important educational function has been neglected up to now, except for minimal efforts by a minuscule staff.

The commission recommends that members of the IRBs be "of diverse backgrounds and sufficient maturity, experience and competence" to be effective and gain the respect of investigators and local communities alike (1978b, p. 13). At least one member of each board should not be otherwise affiliated with the institution. Recognizing the lack of effective continuing review in many instances, the commission recommends that there be continuing review and that research approval be suspended where there is "unexpected serious harm to subjects" (1978b, p. 13).

The commission of course recommends that the present policy of paying attention to risk–benefit ratios and proper methods of obtaining informed consent be continued. It also recommends that the selection of subjects be "equitable," though it does not specify just what this means in practice. In addition to previous standard elements of informed consent, the commission recommends that subjects be informed as to "whether treatment or compensation is available if harm occurs" (1978b, p. 21). This recommendation was accepted by the secretary of HEW; and as of January 2, 1979, this element of informed consent became required by federal regulation. (For an early recommendation of "clinical research insurance," see Ladimer,

1963.) In acknowledgement of the fact that under some conditions, especially those in which there is "no more than minimal risk" and also "scientific merit," the commission recommends that informed consent not always be considered necessary. Finally, and again for certain carefully specified and preapproved categories of research where risk is minimal, the commission recommends that approval be "expedited" by giving the authority of the board to the chairman or to an "experienced reviewer" designated by the chairman. In aid of boards wishing to use expedited review, the commission provides a list of examples (1978b, pp. 33–36).

In sum, the commission has accepted the institutional review board as a valuable and viable formal social control mechanism, but one in need of still further development in the interests both of protecting subjects and of not impeding scientific research. If its recommendations are enacted into regulation or law, a good deal of cooperation from both researchers and the community will be necessary to make them effective. (For further discussions of needed improvements in IRBs, see Lipsett, Fletcher, and Secundy, 1978; Veatch, 1978; and Robertson, 1978.)

Hospital Review Committees and Procedures

Since the behavior and attitudes of physicians with regard to informed consent and the institutional review boards are only specific derivatives and manifestations of their more general behavior and attitudes toward other and older formal social control mechanisms, it will be useful to look at some of them. We start with hospital review committees and procedures, which have the most comprehensive functions for the surveillance of physician performance. Here we can turn to the investigations and judgments of Robert Derbyshire, a physician who has made these matters his special interest since the 1960s and has commented on them in the *Journal of the American Medical Association* (1965, 1974).

Derbyshire feels that the hospitals "during the past few years . . . have definitely improved their disciplinary procedures" for maintaining medical competence (1974). This has occurred, he says, because of actions against hospitals in the law courts and because of the principles set for these matters by the Joint

Commission on the Accreditation of Hospitals. The establishment of tissue, audit, and professional review committees has,
he says, "at least made the hospitals aware that ethical problems do exist" (1974). Nonetheless, "enforcement of professional standards is no better than the effectiveness of the committees, and this varies widely."

Increasingly, because law suits have held hospital administrators responsible for the performance of their medical staff
members, hospital administrations are putting pressure on the
medical committees to operate more actively and effectively.
Many hospitals, Derbyshire holds, "are lax in regard to the physical and psychological standards of staff members. . . . A large
number of hospitals do not demand certificates of competence
from the physician who wishes to resume practice after suffering a severe illness" (1974, p. 59). It has been suggested that
hospital bylaws should require physical examinations of medical staff at specified ages. In addition to physical impairment,
incompetence may be caused by mental illness or alcohol or
drug addiction.

The medical staffs of hospitals have been most reluctant to
control the behavior of members suffering from any of these
disabilities. At the American Medical Association's Third National Conference on the Impaired Physician, held in 1978, the
doctors present "voiced tremendous hostility" to outside control or punishment of such physicians (Annas, 1978; see also
Green, Carroll, and Buxton, 1978). They felt that impaired physicians should be "taken aside" by their fellow physicians and
"convinced in a friendly, non-threatening way to accept treatment." However, "most agreed that . . . physicians hardly ever
do this." Annas concludes with some excellent recommendations for a program for handling "sick" physicians, but acknowledges that "there is also little agreement as to how these
objectives can be accomplished" (1978, p. 19). Such members
of hospital staffs have been allowed to "resign voluntarily" and
without any entry on an official record of the real reason for
resignation. When such a doctor applies elsewhere for admission to a hospital staff, the new hospital has no formal way of
discovering his past delinquency. "The usual reason given privately for this," says Derbyshire, "is that the authorities did not
want to interfere with his means of livelihood." But, he asks
rhetorically, "Should this be permitted? Isn't protection of the

reputation of the physician, when it is a reputation for incompetence, a flagrant disregard of an obligation to protect the welfare of the public?" (1974, p. 62).

A more severe criticism of hospital-based formal control mechanisms for the supervision of physician competence has been made by Millman on the basis of some extensive participant-observer research in three hospitals, all of them private, university-affiliated institutions ranging in size from three hundred fifty to six hundred beds (1977). These hospitals, located in the Northeast and on the West Coast, are all regarded as good hospitals, fully accredited, two of them affiliated with prestigious medical schools. They are definitely not "fringe" hospitals. Millman carried on her research with the full knowledge and approval of the medical staffs. So confident were they of the high standards of their own practices and yet so unknowing of the defects in these practices that they made no efforts to change their usual performances while they were being observed. Millman was thus able to enter many "doctors only" areas of the hospitals, to observe at bedsides and in operating rooms, to talk with physicians during coffee breaks and lunch.

Among her other findings, Millman noted first that what Derbyshire reported more abstractly was certainly the case very concretely in her hospitals. When she asked hospital officials how often doctors were dismissed from the staff for repeated incompetence, she was told dismissal almost never occurred. "Physicians who were openly acknowledged by the chiefs [of services] to be dangerous or incompetent were allowed to remain on the staff and various justifications were cited," she says, such as the fact that they would only set up practices elsewhere, with less supervision and less chance of someone rescuing their victims.

Millman also noted the less than full effectiveness of one of the formal control mechanisms of which hospital staffs are most proud, the monthly medical morbidity and mortality conferences, where uncertainties and errors of diagnosis and prognosis are exposed for entire staffs to see, comment upon, and learn from. Millman came to feel that at these conferences either mistakes were too often not so much acknowledged as implicitly denied or blame was spread around so much that it evaporated or was laid upon the shoulders of "uncooperative or neurotic" patients. Millman quotes the chief of medicine at one hospital, the physician in charge of the "mortality review," as saying that most medical mistakes cannot be discussed at a review because "it's got to be a cordial affair." According to this physician, "80 percent of the mistakes made around here are ignored or swept under the rug." Such allegations are certainly impressionistic and probably exaggerated, but there is no doubt that the formal and public mechanisms for reviewing errors and mistakes in hospitals are less than fully effective. A little more outside participation, perhaps by physicians from other hospitals, might improve them.

Because he knows about the present defects of hospital review committees as social control mechanisms, but because he is worried about the costs that "outside" formal controls entail for the process of medical care and about the ways in which physicians can successfully evade them, David Mechanic, one of our leading medical sociologists who is much concerned for better social policy in this field, has recommended that hospital review committees be supplemented by more effective patient grievance procedures and by the presence of ombudsmen in every hospital (1978, pp. 31–35). Mechanic starts with the fact that patients increasingly use medical institutions "for which there are no alternatives. Thus, if they feel their rights violated they have little recourse but to complain directly to the providers, withdraw from using services, or initiate litigation." Patients are reluctant to complain directly to the powerful provider; there is often not much responsiveness even when they do. Withdrawal is not usually possible; and litigation, despite the proliferation of malpractice suits, is something few of the aggrieved can pursue because of its social, psychological, and monetary costs. In addition, many justifiable complaints are not even actionable at law—complaints about needless waiting, shunting about, and impersonal care. "What is needed in any sizable program," says Mechanic, "is a grievance procedure through which patients who feel wronged can make their problems and concerns known." If such a procedure existed, he feels, there could be relatively rapid mobilization to deal with these problems early in their development; it would also provide an opportunity to give necessary information and help to patients who have unrealistic or misguided expectations. Mechanic feels that such a procedure would be effective only if it had strong administrative support and were highly visible and easily accessible to patients. The procedure would permit the informal resolution of many difficulties that arise in patient care, "but under some conditions more formal procedures will be required." Mechanic also feels that the grievance procedure should include consumers or consumer representatives, not just medical staff, though it may also happen that staff members would want to "initiate grievances concerning failures and inadequacies of care in the program." Staff members are often aware of abuses and problems but have no way of communicating their concerns. The grievance procedure would both sensitize health professionals to patients' perceptions and act as a deterrent to some abuses. Where there is a "serious" process for handling grievances, Mechanic thinks, it "contributes to the consumer's sense of trust that the program is accountable."

As for ombudsmen, Mechanic feels that they too would improve communication, prevent the escalation of misunderstanding, and assist patients in dealing with the powerful professionals. Both grievance procedures and ombudsmen "contribute to reducing the inequality" of understanding and power between patient and physician.

Medical Society Ethics Committees and State Licensing Boards

Beyond the hospital review committees and procedures lie the further formal social control mechanisms of the American Medical Association's county medical societies' ethics committees and the state medical licensing boards. These are supposed to transcend the particularisms of each hospital and locality. Neither has much effectiveness in controlling the incompetent physician because of the unwillingness of the medical profession to exercise the kind of self-regulation on which it rests its claim to authority and special privilege.

As for effective control by the A.M.A.'s local medical societies and their appointed committees, "When grievance committees were first inaugurated," says Derbyshire, "they were hailed as representing a great step forward. They have not lived up to their potentials, however. Notable is their lack of initiative and action so that their main function is the adjudication of disputes over fees and squabbles between physicians" (1974, p. 61). The county medical societies have been so ineffective in performing their disciplinary functions that in 1969 the Department of Medical Ethics of the A.M.A. abandoned its program of having these local groups report their disciplinary actions to the parent association. "A large number of societies reported no action at all, while others submitted incomplete reports. The latest figures available were for 1968 when 33 states' medical societies reported no procedures whatsoever" (Derbyshire, 1974, p. 62). Joining Derbyshire, but supporting his judgments through impressions rather than evidence of a more systematic kind, another physician has commented:

> Medical societies appear to have been reluctant to tackle tough problems relating to questionable actions by their members. It is amazing how many excuses can be found for not conducting an investigation or for not taking action. One common excuse is that if the medical society becomes involved it will be sued. Another is that "a matter of judgment" is involved and one cannot fault judgmental decisions of a fellow physician. Neither excuse is more than that—it is merely an excuse. The profession must not rely on excuses (Holman, 1973, p. 562).

Dr. Holman is concerned that such ineffective self-regulation destroys public faith in the medical profession and such loss of faith may lead to "restrictive judicial and statutory regulations." Ethical scandals have been reported in the press in New York City, for example, with clear evidence that the facts were known to local physicians who nonetheless took no action through their medical society ethics committee. It is not surprising that there has indeed been a loss of faith and a call for state regulation. In New York State, as we have already noted, a statute now mandates the reporting by physicians of dangerous and unethical behavior on the part of colleagues on pain of punishment where nonreporting can be proved.

Finally, even at the highest level of formal and legal control over the medical profession, the state licensing boards, we find a mechanism for the regulation of incompetence and unethical behavior that is less than fully effective. "The boards should be the final guardians of the public," says Derbyshire, who then asks, "are they?" and answers his own question, "on the whole, no" (1974, p. 62). The answer is based on Derbyshire's examination of the evidence on disciplinary actions taken by these state boards. During a ten-year period from the early 1960s to the early 1970s, Derbyshire found, only two-thirds of 1 percent of approximately three hundred thousand physicians in the United States "had difficulty with licensing boards." The figures make "one wonder," he says, " how many unethical physicians go undetected and unpunished." Like Holman, he concludes, "The medical profession has long insisted that it can best police its own ranks, and it should. Yet, unless all of the agencies involved in medical discipline work together to improve their methods, outsiders conceivably could take over the control of medical discipline" (1974, p. 62).

According to a later report than Derbyshire's, the effectiveness of state licensing boards may slowly be increasing, apparently against the grosser cases of medical misfeasance. In a survey made by the American Medical Association in 1978 covering some fifty-five out of sixty state licensing boards (some states have two boards, one for regular physicians, another for osteopaths), it was discovered that the number of disciplinary actions taken by these boards increased from 119 in 1971 to 685 in 1977 (*New York Times,* December 2, 1978). In this period, the number of physicians in the United States had increased, but in much smaller proportion than the increase in disciplinary actions. The actions taken include revocation of licenses, suspension of narcotics permits, censure, and denial of license reciprocity from one state to another. According to the executive vice president of the American Medical Association, this increase in disciplinary action may be attributable to the steadily increasing number of states which, like New York, now provide immunity from civil liability for persons reporting errant physicians to state boards. "Historically," says Dr. Sammons, "physicians who have reported colleagues to disciplinary boards have exposed themselves to the possibility of a suit for libel or slander. With more and more states granting immunity to people who in good faith report to state boards, the number of disciplinary actions which have been initiated have also increased" (*New York Times,* December 2, 1978). Thus the effectiveness of formal mechanisms for control of the medical profession may be improved somewhat, though probably the primary improvement must occur in the informal mechanisms if there is to be considerable improvement in physician performance. This is certainly the sentiment of practicing physicians and researchers. It remains for them to take the initiative in strengthening these informal mechanisms.

MEDICAL MALPRACTICE AGAIN

In this chapter, we have seen that there are defects in the present system of medical socialization and social control, both formal and informal, for the creation and maintenance of effective ethical principles and practice with regard to informed consent and related issues. The problem is clear: how to improve the system while preserving necessary and desirable levels of professional autonomy in both therapy and research. Outside initiatives from government and other social actors have been taken and should continue, but a considerable amount of new initiatives from within the profession itself is clearly essential. Before turning away from this discussion, we can give one final example of how lacking effective professional self-regulation often is and how such self-regulation could be a powerful force. Our example is the case of medical malpractice; our discussion is based on some excellent evidence.

One study of the records of patients discharged from two hospitals in 1972 showed a large number of serious injuries resulting from malpractice; of these, only one in fifteen actually led to a malpractice claim; moreover, 40 percent of the file entries held by malpractice insurance companies refer to mishaps reported by physicians but never followed up in action by patients (cited in Schwartz and Komesar, 1978). Obviously, considerable incompetence and delinquency occurs in medical practice, more than appears in what is called the "epidemic" of recent malpractice suits. Another study supports this conclusion by showing that of approximately twenty-four thousand incidents of malpractice detected in hospital records in California, at most only one out of every six or seven results in a malpractice claim (cited in Schwartz and Komesar, 1978). Patients who sue, moreover, do not do so at random, whether justly or unjustly, according to a study sponsored by the Rand Corporation and carried out by a physician, William B. Schwartz, and a law professor, Neil K. Komesar (1978). In their study of eight thousand physicians in the Los Angeles area during a four-year period, they found that forty-six physicians, or six-tenths of 1 percent, accounted for 10 percent of all malpractice claims and for 30 percent of all payments made. The average number of suits against these forty-six physicians was one and one-quarter per year. There is clearly a small set of highly visible, incompetent physicians. Under the sway of their excessively rationalist economic theory of behavior, Schwartz and Komesar recommend that the solution to this problem is differential pricing of malpractice insurance, charging the clearly and continuously delinquent physician the higher rates. Perhaps this remedy would have some effect, but it hardly seems compatible with the medical profession's proclaimed ethical standards. It is not exactly a professional solution to a professional problem. A professional solution would be more effective self-regulation by doctors than now exists. Long before medical malpractice recurs among the visibly delinquent, there should be professional remedies to prevent it. Where prevention is not wholly effective, there should be professional agencies to which patients could resort for redress of the physical and ethical harms done to them. By controlling perennial delinquents and by strengthening the ethics committees of county medical societies, physicians would be on much stronger moral and political grounds in their claims for professional autonomy.

7

Informed Consent and Special Populations

$\mathbb{A}$ special opportunity to examine present principles and practices of informed consent in biomedical research is provided by certain special populations in which experimentation is often carried out. Prisoners (often termed a "captive" population), children, and the mentally infirm, when used as experimental subjects, highlight the moral and practical problems of obtaining informed consent from normal populations. These special populations, or what Robert Veatch has called "Group II Subjects," are those among whom, he says, "self-determination is either impossible or constrained" (1978b, p. 35). Remember that for Veatch, and quite properly so, the moral right of self-determination is the basic principle on which informed consent is based. In this chapter, using the analytic concepts from our previous chapters—values and norms, laws, authority patterns, communication structures, and social control mechanisms—we shall look at the problems of informed consent in these special populations, partly because they are of interest in themselves, but partly because they help us to understand the situation among normal populations. That they are of great moral interest in themselves, that they are special new social problems, is indicated by the fact that Public Law 93-348, which established the National Commission for the Protection of Human Subjects of Biomedical and Behavioral Research, specifically mandated the new commission to look into the special problems of prisoners, children, and the mentally infirm. The commission's reports and many documents commissioned by and submitted to it are now available; they are an essential resource for our discussion in this chapter (1976; 1977; 1978a).

PRISONERS AND INFORMED CONSENT

The use of prisoners as subjects in biomedical experimentation is a peculiarly, indeed uniquely, American practice and social problem. (See National Commission, 1976; Mitford, 1974; Jonsen et al., 1975; American Correctional Association, 1976). Since the 1960s, there have been increasingly vigorous expressions of moral outrage against it, culminating in the congressional mandate of 1974 to the National Commission for the Protection of Human Subjects to make a special inquiry into this problem and produce a special set of recommendations for future policy. In no other country in the world are prisoners used as biomedical research subjects, partly because of the horror aroused by the Nazi use of prisoners during World War II, a horror expressed in the ban on such use of prisoners in one of the provisions of the Nuremberg Code, and partly, it seems, because adequate facilities for such use of prisoners have never been established in prisons outside the United States. A survey sponsored by the national commission and carried out in 1975 by a physician and an official of the pharmaceutical company, Merck, Sharp & Dohme, found that in seven European countries (Belgium, France, Germany, Holland, Italy, Spain, and Sweden), five English-speaking countries (Australia, Canada, New Zealand, South Africa, and the United Kingdom), four Latin American countries (Brazil, Colombia, Mexico, and Peru), and Japan, no research is conducted on prisoners. The survey found that in most countries volunteers for medical experiments are drawn from among students, civil servants (military, police, and firemen), and medical and paramedical personnel.

Prisoners had been used sporadically in the United States and elsewhere as subjects of medical research before World War II, but it was only then that the systematic and extensive use of prisoners began. Ironically, because values were different at that time, this new use of prisoners was approved by both prisoners and others. In a country almost wholly united in the war effort, prisoners too were patriotic and volunteered to make their contribution by serving as subjects for the testing of synthetic antimalarial drugs to replace the supply of quinine cut off by the war. Prisoners could feel that they were participating in some way in the dangers experienced by their fellow countrymen fighting in the Pacific theater of war. Dr. John D. Arnold started his antimalarial research with prisoners at that time and continued it for more than twenty-five years, only finally to give it up and turn to alternative "cloistered populations." He notes that

> the use of inmates in American prisons for medical research developed primarily during World War II under what was then thought to be the exigencies of wartime. From a scientific point of view, this was an important landmark in that much of the work done in prisons was designed to forestall complications and inadequacies of new drugs, vaccines, and procedures for the ultimate consumer, namely, the American soldier, sailor and airman (Arnold, 1976, p. 7).

Although there was some small moral protest against the use of prisoners at that time, state commissions and other committees, especially the Ivy Commission appointed by Governor Green of Illinois, responded to the protest with their moral approval. Indeed, so widespread was the view that the use of prisoners as volunteers was morally salutary for them that the American Medical Association wanted to deprive prisoners guilty of certain heinous crimes of this special moral privilege. In 1952, the American Medical Association's House of Delegates passed a resolution expressing its disapproval "of the participation in scientific experiments of persons convicted of murder, rape, arson, kidnapping, treason, or other heinous crimes."

Once the system and facilities for using American prisoners were in place as a result of the war period, and without the strong and continued moral protest that arose later, the system was maintained and extended for a number of practical reasons. Cloistered populations, over which a variety of necessary controls can be exercised, are convenient for experimentation, and prisoners provided such a population ready to hand. The cost and difficulty of assembling other controlled populations, though not excessive (as we shall see when we consider some alternatives to the use of prisoners), made the use of prisoners seem highly desirable. This was especially so because the number of new drugs requiring testing increased considerably in the postwar period. This increase was caused partly by the increased rate of biomedical research and pharmaceutical development and partly by the fact that the Food and Drug Administration regulations for drug testing require what John Arnold calls "a uniquely American procedure," Phase I testing. Phase I testing, which is not required in other countries, is an exercise in which a new drug is tried out on normal (volunteer) humans, after extensive animal testing, to determine human toxicity, metabolism, absorption, elimination, preferred route of administration, and safe dosage. In Phase I testing, small single doses of a compound are given to a small number of subjects. The size of the dosage is then increased in gradual increments in continuous trials. The action of the drugs and the safety of the subjects can be watched closely. In John Arnold's experience, despite elaborate testing in animals, about one-third of more than three hundred new compounds studied by his research group showed properties not easily predicted from the animal studies. These properties ranged from the trivial to the potentially fatal. Since the amount of Phase I testing increased considerably after World War II, prisoners came more and more to be used as this first test site. It has been estimated by the Pharmaceutical Manufacturers Association that in 1975 85 percent of all Phase I testing was done on prisoners.

How common is the use of prisoners as research subjects? A survey of the Federal Bureau of Prisons and all the state prison agencies conducted in 1975 by the national commission discovered the following facts. Note that county and municipal prisons, where conditions are generally worse than those in state prisons, were not included in the survey and that the survey was made at a time when various legal and legislative actions had already been taken to ban the use of prisoners either temporarily or permanently. Although twenty-one states permitted biomedical research in prisons, it was actually being carried on in only seven states. Eight states explicitly prohibited such research—one by legislation, six by departmental policy, and one by moratorium; twenty-three states have no specific policies about research in prisons. Further evidence on the extent of the use of prisoners as subjects is provided in a survey of its members by the Pharmaceutical Manufacturers Association. Fifty-one companies, representing three-fourths of the members' annual expenditures for research and development, answered the questionnaire. Sixteen of the respondents used prisoners. That there are alternatives to prisoners as subjects is indicated by the reports from the companies that they also use college students, medical students, company employees, residents of foreign countries, military personnel, members of fraternal organizations, medical personnel, and the general population as subjects. Of the sixteen who reported the use of prisoners, most conducted Phase I testing; they used a total of thirty-six hundred prisoners in one hundred protocols studying seventy-one different compounds.

For some opponents of the use of prisoners, of course, the actual extent of the practice is unimportant; for them, *any* use of prisoners is immoral. Value judgments, as we have seen, have always surrounded the use of prisoners. The Nuremberg Code expressed its moral horror of the practice, and in the United States it was justified during the war by its patriotic and altruistic purposes. Value differences are still at the heart of the conflict between the proponents and opponents of the practice. Although proponents often talk in terms of the utilitarian and practical functions of the research for the prisoners and for society, central to their position is a concern with certain values and rights that ought to be preserved for prisoners even in a situation that deprives them of so much. Proponents feel that prisoners ought to have left to them a certain measure, however small, of their right to freedom and autonomy, some scope for choice in a highly constrained world (Cohen, 1978). The opportunity to volunteer for research gives them scope for at least that minimal exercise of their right to be free, to have some autonomy, to choose to volunteer or not.

Those who absolutely oppose any use of prisoners in research also speak in the name of values. Their value, they feel, is more fundamental than the lesser values of which proponents speak—the value of human "personhood," of individual integrity, of personal inviolability, as it is variously phrased. This value precedes and overrides all others, not least of all those lesser virtues claimed for prison research. Opponents of prison research feel that prisons are inherently too large a violation of "personhood," of the integrity of the individual, to permit such further encroachments upon it as the practice of using prisoner subjects. The value conflict, then, the moral issue, is between greater and lesser values, as different groups judge them. In its final recommendations, the national commission gave the greater weight to the greater value, the importance of individual integrity, but it also gave some weight to the lesser values by specifying a series of stringent conditions under which it was morally justifiable to use prisoners for biomedical research.

When proponents of the use of prisoners in research argue their case, they usually do not speak explicitly of values but detail a list of what they call the "motives" of the prisoners for wanting to volunteer. The list of motives is usually some mixture of the individual purposes and social goals that such volunteering might serve. Dr. Frank Ayd, who has been a proponent of the use of prisoners for some years, has compiled a list of eleven reasons for volunteering by prisoners:

> The most often cited reasons for a prisoner's willingness to be an experimental subject are (1) financial reward; (2) hope for a reduction in the sentence; (3) direct or indirect seeking of medical or psychiatric help through professional advice or a drug; (4) to escape a lonely, tedious existence; (5) to have something to do and talk about; (6) to participate in what is looked upon as a stimulating, exciting adventure; (7) a desire to prove to himself and to others that he can do something good and admirable; (8) to command and receive respect and accolades . . . ; (9) the absence of obligations to others; (10) some form of psychopathology . . . to gratify self-destructive urges; and, (11) simple curiosity (Ayd, 1973, p; 9, see also Ayd, 1972; Ayd and Blackwell, eds., 1971; McDonald, 1967; Hodges and Bean, 1967; Martin et al., 1968; and Arnold, Martin, and Boyer, 1970.)

Although Ayd and other proponents of prisoner research provide no systematic evidence on the existence and strength of these various motives, they seem plausible; moreover, when evidence is collected systematically, it supports Ayd's claims. For example, in a study sponsored by the national commission, the Survey Research Center at the University of Michigan interviewed 181 different individuals in four prisons; all of these prisoners had participated in research projects as volunteers. (Tannenbaum and Cooke, 1976.) Although the participants gave many "reasons" or "motives," such as better living conditions, need for a good medical evalution, and the desire to perform a worthwhile service for others—motives not dissimilar from those listed by Ayd—it was clear that the overriding motivation was the money they received for participating. Here too the findings were in agreement with Ayd, who put "financial reward" first on his list.

All these motives, especially money, seem to be either less important or morally abhorrent to the opponents of the use of prisoners. One philosopher, who is a strong opponent, expresses her moral outrage at the use of the money motive in the following way: "For where the money motive predominates in the decision to volunteer as an experimental subject, make no mistake, we are dealing with prostitution—the selling of one's body for financial gain. . . . Where the money motive predominates among prisoners, experimenters may be seen as solicitors of human flesh and prisoners may be viewed as prostitutes" (Cook, 1976, pp. 31, 55). It should be noted that none of the usual "motives," not even the money one, is universal among the prisoners or always powerful enough to induce them to volunteer. The study of men in four prisons conducted by the Survey Research Center also interviewed nonparticipants in research and discovered that some of them strongly disapproved of research in prison.

The importance of values in the conflict over the use of prisoners in research comes out nowhere more clearly than in the emphasis opponents put upon the *voluntariness* of participation. For them, the statement of the Nuremberg Code, "The *voluntary* consent of the human subject is absolutely essential," is the final and fundamental word. The absence of voluntariness violates the value of "personhood" or individual integrity. Where voluntariness does not exist, as they maintain it cannot in the inherently coercive environment of prisons, then other virtues are not compelling. For example, the philosopher, Roy Branson of the Kennedy Institute of Bioethics at Georgetown University says that the "motive" of altruism attributed to prisoners by proponents of research does not count because "the expression of that altruism through participation in research is insufficiently voluntary" (Branson, 1976, p. 9). Another philosopher puts the value of voluntariness higher than that of information: "The crucial ethical emphasis . . . lies with the voluntary nature of consent, not with the informational aspect. Notice that when we speak of informed consent, it always makes sense to ask whether it has been freely given; but if we speak of voluntary consent we can neither ask whether it has been freely given nor whether it is informed" (Cook, 1976, p. 13). By reminding us that voluntariness, not consent, is the heart of the matter for prisoners, Cook is also asking us to see that the same is true for all research subjects, even those outside prisons. There is always some degree of coerciveness in all consent situations. Information is not an end in itself, but only a means to achieving a greater degree of voluntariness. It is an important means, as we have seen throughout this book, but the case of prisoners makes it clear how being informed stands in relation to serving voluntarily. We shall return to this point when we discuss how well informed prisoners in fact are.

Since the 1960s, not only has the use of prisoners for biomedical research been increasingly criticized on value grounds but a variety of statutory and legal prohibitions have followed after. Eight states and the Federal Bureau of Prisons have taken various formal steps to end the practice. Moreover, in just about all states that do permit research, the enabling statute or regulation explicitly requires that informed consent must be obtained. Unfortunately, in regard to other provisions, the state rules vary considerably. As one legal specialist in this area, George Annas of Boston University, has put it, they range "from excellent to non-existent" (Annas, Glantz, and Katz, 1976, p. 42). There is obviously need for further change in the law to catch up with changing values, either to ban use of prisoners outright or to provide better protections where such use is still permitted. As the law now stands, Annas has concluded after his detailed summary of existing legal provisions in this area, there is no general principle that prohibits the use of prisoners: "If, however, it is decided that prisoners are a proper population on which to perform biomedical and behavioral research, it is our conclusion that the law will not bar such participation, provided that the safeguards discussed in this paper are adopted" (Annas, Glantz, and Katz, 1976, p. 53).

There is some hope, of course, that the principles and practice of the use of prisoners will change as a result of the recommendations of the National Commission, which we shall look at shortly, and of the consequent transformation of these recommendations into regulations by the Department of Health, Education, and Welfare. The DHEW regulations, of course, affect only federally funded use of prisoners, either in federal prisons or in state prisons where federal funds are being used by medical researchers. Since the states have autonomy, only they can speak the final regulatory word where private industry or the state itself provides the research funds. Opponents of the use of prisoners in research will have to pursue their goals at the state and local levels, as indeed they have in several states already. The Prison Project of the American Civil Liberties Union, for example, has been active in this regard in Connecticut and Maryland at least.

Beyond the law's protections, of course, we have to examine the actual authority and power structures in prisons to understand what goes on there and how this might affect the use of prisoners as research subjects. The protections of the law interact both with the inherently coercive nature of prison life and with what the national commission in its report calls the "potential for arbitrary exercise of authority by prison officials" in a "closed" situation (1976, p. 5). This point of arbitrary power is made more specific by the sociologist, John Irwin, in his report to the commission on how the structure of power in prisons affects the possibility of informed consent:

> Arbitrary, discriminatory, and partial decision making . . . is virtually endemic in prisons. Prison officials have been granted wide discretionary powers in order to "rehabilitate" prisoners, maintain control and incapacitate "dangerous" individuals. Too often they use this discretionary power to make arbitrary decisions in order to punish persons for acts which have not been proven against them, to reward persons who fall into their favor, and to isolate persons who they find troublesome or repulsive. . . . The prison has developed this arbitrary decision making mode to the extreme because they have been granted considerable autonomy and wider discretionary powers as a result of their special task—handling convicted felons—a task which is seen as particularly difficult and potentially explosive. Society in effect has thrust this task upon the prison administrators and asked only that they keep it out of sight (1976, pp. 6–7).

There is more to power in prison than the arbitrary official structure. All prisons develop, usually with the knowledge and even the encouragement of the official structure, what the sociologists of prison life call "the inmate power structure." A small number of prisoners runs a power structure that keeps the rest in line, carrying out punishments and granting rewards just as the official structure does. The official structure often permits some access to the few goods of prison life to go uncontrolled by itself and therefore to be available to the inmate power structure. Access to certain jobs and opportunities, including such goods as being research subjects, can be under the control of the inmate power structure. All the studies of prison life show that this structure can be almost as arbitrary and brutal as the official structure. Violence, homosexual rape, and blackmail may be permitted by the inmate power structure (Davis, 1972). This is the background against which we must understand the "voluntary" character of consent in prison research.

Our understanding of both the official and the inmate power structures in prison permit us to clarify a controversy between opponents and proponents of the use of prisoners in research about whether prisons are what Erving Goffman called "total institutions." It is clear that if "total institutions" implies some absolute control by officials with no power at all left to the inmates, then prisons do not fall under such an absolutist definition. Inmates have some residual control over their daily lives and their rewards and punishments. But if the term signifies the tremendous power over inmates wielded by the combined forces of the official and the inmate power structures, then the term carries a meaning not far from the actual reality of prison life. One way or the other, the prisoner's freedom of choice is very small.

How shall we then deal with the fact that prisoners who volunteer for research say that they do not "feel" coerced? In their study of prisoners participating in research, Tannenbaum and Cooke found that "the great majority of subjects agreed that their participation in the research project about which they were being interviewed was voluntary" (1976, p. 53). The philosopher Branson does not accept these "feelings" as conclusive proof of voluntarism. "That some prisoners themselves are satisfied with the opportunity to be involved in experimentation is not conclusive evidence that they actually have sufficient freedom to consent. To be sufficiently free it is not enough that one is free from feeling he is coerced" (1977, p. 15). Only the availability of "genuine alternatives" to volunteering would be sufficient proof that it was an expression of "personhood" and not of coercion from the prison's power system. Here again, the situation of research subjects in prisons reminds us of an important fact about the consent of so-called "free" subjects who enter into therapy or research. Because they are so often also based on ignorance, indirect coercion, or fear, their feelings are not enough basis for genuine voluntariness to exist. We must understand the actual system of medical relationships, and especially its power aspects, to make a good judgment about voluntary and informed consent.

Because of the great, almost exclusive emphasis on the questions of voluntariness and powerful coercion in discussions of the morality of using prisoners in research, relatively little attention is paid to the problem of communications with them, of how well they are informed by the biomedical researchers who work in prison populations. This is in great contrast, as we have seen in Chapter 5, to the discussion dealing with "free-world" patients and subjects. There, communication is to the fore, the problem of coercion is assumed away. Probably prisoner subjects, despite the direct and indirect forms of power that affect them, are no worse informed, and no better, than their free-world counterparts. Certainly, the evidence we have seems to support this general view, though no explicit comparison between the two groups has ever been made. When Tannenbaum and Cooke (1976) interviewed both the research investigators and the prisoner participants in four prisons, they found the following to be the case: first, consent forms were used with all prisoners in all studies; in addition, research investigators said, they provided an oral explanation of the study to all subjects. Investigators reported to Tannenbaum and Cooke that they spend an average of thirty-three minutes with subjects on each project explaining the study and getting consent. Most of the investigators said they were personally involved in getting consent. Nearly all the consent forms mentioned the purpose of the study, some with detailed descriptions, others including only the bare statement of purpose. Nearly all consent forms describe the procecures to be followed and the expected risks and benefits. None of the forms, however, give a statement about compensation for harmful effects that may occur. Finally, as is also true in many free-world consent forms, when the prison consent forms are judged on the Flesch Readability Yardstick, they are found to be difficult to read, not only because of technical terms but because the sentences are too long and complex. In sum, researchers in prisons, except perhaps for the compensation item, seem to be using the same consent forms and communicating in the same way as they do with their nonprison subjects. As we have seen, in the prison populations communications become less important than the fact that the prisoners are inherently unfree and without alternatives.

As for review boards and other mechanisms of social control over the biomedical researchers in prisons, these also appear to be no worse and no better than those outside. In their survey of actual prison practices, Tannenbaum and Cooke (1976) found that review procedures were somewhat different in the five prisons where they studied them. The review process included, in different combinations in the different prisons, the institutional review boards of the organizations from which the biomedical researchers came, review committees established by state departments of corrections or by the local prison authorities, and committees created by the drug companies sponsoring the research. In some of the review procedures, biomedical, legal, or prisoner representatives were involved. Tannenbaum and Cooke found that few research protocols were rejected, but a great many were modified at least slightly, chiefly as to the wording of the consent forms, much as is the case with free-world review boards. Investigators reported that they felt the review process worked smoothly; in part because there was little turnover in the membership of the review boards and definite mutual expectations were established. On outside review boards, there is more turnover. Finally, as is also true outside, little monitoring of the actual conduct of the research exists; the members of review boards make what are apparently casual visits to the prisons from time to time. It is certainly not true that review is more stringent in prisons than elsewhere, although this should probably be the case.

As we have indicated earlier, in its final recommendations for a policy on the use of prisoners as subjects in biomedical research, the national commission recognized the value conflicts inherent in such use, gave the larger moral weight to the value of preserving the "personhood" or integrity of the prisoner in his inescapably coercive environment, and yet gave some weight to his rights and needs in that environment by stipulating a whole set of conditions in which it would be morally acceptable to use prisoners. (For an excellent account of how the commission came to its conclusions, see Branson, 1977.) As is immediately clear from the stipulations, their chief purpose is to reduce the coerciveness of prison life. As the commission put it, "should coercions be lessened and more equitable systems for the sharing of burdens and benefits be devised, respect for persons and concern for justice would suggest that prisoners not be deprived of the opportunity to participate in research" (1976, p. 8). Chief among the commission's stipulations is the requirement that decent *alternatives* to "volunteering" for research be provided the prisoner. Other and more attractive forms of work than are presently offered in prison would clearly constitute such alternatives. The commission also added other conditions to improve "voluntariness": "Minimum conditions for such voluntariness and openness include adequate living conditions, provisions for effective redress of grievances, separation of research participation from parole considerations, and public scrutiny" (1976, p. 16). It is significant that in the eight pages of its report in which the commission states its recommendations in full, only one short paragraph is devoted directly to informed consent: "In negotiations regarding consent, it should be determined that the written or verbal comprehensibility of the information presented is appropriate to the subject population" (p. 20). Information, the commission is convinced, is definitely subordinate to voluntariness, only a means to that end. This is an important point for the understanding of informed consent in all biomedical research situations.

CHILDREN AND INFORMED CONSENT

For a number of reasons, the use of children as subjects in biomedical research has become a social problem, a focus of conflicting values and interests, during the last twenty years. (On the historical background of use of children, see Mitchell, 1964.) First, even in the best of circumstances, infants, children, and adolescents to some extent, have a social incompetence and vulnerability that calls for special consideration and protection in both custom and law. Second, during the recent past, reaching into many different areas where children are involved, not just in medical research but in the school and the family as well, what we may call the *children's rights* movement has been seeking to strengthen the rights of children against all groups that are in a position to abuse them, from the state itself to their parents. "Child advocacy," as Kahn, Kamerman, and McGowan call it in their survey of the children's rights movement, grew considerably during the period of general social reform of the 1960s. It represented:

> a series of efforts to meet with children's unmet needs in one or more of the following ways: affirming new concepts of legal entitlements; offering needed services in areas where none existed; persisting in the provision of services when other more conventional programs dropped cases; assuring access to entitlements and help; mediating between children or families and institutions such as schools, health facilities, and courts; and facilitating self-organization among deprived community groups, adolescents, or parents of handicapped children (1972, p. 9.)

Indeed, in 1971, President Nixon assigned to the Office of Child Development in the Department of Health, Education, and Welfare the task of establishing a national center for child advocacy. For the problem of children being used as subjects in biomedical research, the child advocacy movement culminated in the special legislative mandate to the National Commission for the Protection of the Human Subjects of Biomedical and Behavioral Research that it should "identify the requirements for informed consent to participation in biomedical and behavioral research by children." Along with prisoners and the mentally infirm, children were singled out for special attention by the commission, over and beyond its general mandate to protect the population at large. Following on its report and recommendations for prisoners, the commission has produced another report and set of recommendations for the problem of children in research (1977; for a critique and an account of how the commission came to its conclusions, see McCartney, 1978).

On the other side, countering the possibility of their misuse as research subjects and their consequent need for special protection, are the large and undeniable needs and benefits arising from using children in research. Those who argue for the continuing use of children as subjects have pointed out these needs and benefits in great detail; the commission's report explains the variety and force of this argument. The reasons for using children can be grouped into two categories: the lack of an alternative population of suitable research subjects and the harmful consequences of not using children. As to the lack of an alternative population, it is sometimes the case, as with Down's syndrome or cystic fibrosis, that these diseases do not occur in animals, and only children can be used. Moreover, even in conditions where there can be animal pretesting, humans must eventually be used since their responses to similar drugs and regimens for similar disorders often differ from those of animals. Why not use adult populations instead of children, then? Again, diseases unique to children, such as hyaline membrane disease or erythroblastosis fetalis, obviously cannot be studied in adults. Indeed, some disorders are peculiar to childhood subpopulations, to infants, schoolchildren, or teen-agers; and these different stages of childhood must all be studied with the appropriate populations. Finally, even where the same disease occurs in both children and adults, the results of drug dosages with antibiotics and other agents tested in adults cannot be directly extrapolated to children. There is no simple, uniform, and direct scale for drug and other treatments between children and adults. For some time, when necessary scaling of dosages for children of drugs used in adults could not be made with appropriate tests, children were referred to by such distinguished physicians as Dr. Harry Shirkey as "therapeutic orphans" (Shirkey, 1972).

As to the harmful consequences of not involving children in research, there are a number of these. Prohibiting the use of children in research on new treatments for diseases that affect children would, as we have noted, make them therapeutic orphans. Indeed, because children become adults and because some adult diseases (such as atherosclerosis) start in childhood, the failure to use children in research would also harm them as adults. Finally, in the absence of research and testing, many new drugs and other innovative regimens used on children to treat their disorders are later discovered to have seriously harmful consequences. For example, when high concentrations of oxygen were given to all premature infants with hyaline membrane disease without controlled testing, many became blind because of retrolental fibroplasia caused by the toxic effect of high oxygen levels on the blood vessels supplying the retina:

> In sum, there is historical evidence of undesirable consequences resulting from the introduction of innovations in pediatric practice without adequate research, and there are many areas of inquiry that are important for improving the health and well-being of children [and adults], and for which there is no research population other than children (National Commission for the Protection of Human Subjects, 1977, p. 25).

In remarking the fact that even infants, schoolchildren, and teen-agers differ significantly for medical and research purposes, we have touched upon an important question usually raised early on in discussions of the problem of using children in research: What is a child? Since different answers are given to this question in different legal and social circumstances, the commission gives the following definition: "*Children* are persons who have not attained the legal age of consent to general medical care as determined under the applicable law of the jurisdiction in which the research will be conducted" (1977, p. 3). As we shall see, because different legal jurisdictions give different answers under different circumstances, the commission had to use this abstract definition. Within this very general definition, there is the further problem of defining biomedical and social categories, such as infant, schoolchild, and teen-ager. Here again, in the absence of extensive research on the matter, there are different definitions. We shall later see the commission making some hard but important decisions about when "a child" is mature enough to give "assent" to being used as a research subject. An essential point made by the commission and others is that not only physiologically but morally the child must be seen as *developing,* not remaining a simple or static being. It is of the utmost importance to the problem of informed consent in children used as research subjects that their "evolving autonomy" be acknowledged, that "mature minors" be treated differently in matters of consent from immature infants or schoolchildren. Consent is quite different in these different periods of childhood.

How much use of children in research is there? In the Survey

Research Center's study of actual practices in this area for the national commission, a study of a national sample of biomedical research institutions, it was found that in 28 percent of all the projects reviewed by the institutional review boards of this sample from July 1974 to June 1975 at least 25 percent of the subjects were under nineteen years of age (Tannenbaum and Cooke, 1977, p. 2). In its own survey of government agencies' research activities involving children during fiscal 1975, the commission found that all the National Institutes of Health and several other government agencies sponsored research on children. Not only the Institute of Child Health and Human Development; but the Institute of Dental Research; the Institute of General Medical Sciences; the Institute of Neurological and Communicative Disorders; the Heart, Lung and Blood Institute; the Institute of Arthritis, Metabolism, and Digestive Diseases; the Institute of Environmental Health Sciences; the Institute of Mental Health; the Institute on Drug Abuse; the Maternal and Child Health Services of the Public Health Service; the Bureau of Biologics in the Food and Drug Administration; the Department of Agriculture; and the Department of Defense's military hospitals—all sponsored research on children. The problem of informed consent for this research is not small.

We see then that there are good reasons both for and against using children in research. Different values are in conflict and have to be better accommodated to one another than they now are. The key value that underlies all discussions of the problems of informed consent is the value variously called "personhood," autonomy of the individual, or integrity of the individual. In a paper prepared for the commission, Ferguson begins her statement of fundamental principles in the following way:

> First, the child is a *person*. This implies that she/he is not a chattel of his parents, of the state or of any other institution of the society, but has rights as an individual to respect, to privacy, to legal protection, and to consideration as a valuable member of society. Also implied is a reasonable balance between the various views of the child as vulnerable and dependent and as a rational and moral being (Ferguson, 1977, p. 1).

Personhood or autonomy in children is a developing condition. As the child develops from infancy to childhood to the teens, the process of informed consent must more and more acknowledge his or her maturing moral capacity and increasing autonomy. Although children are to be considered persons from birth on, despite their need for some measure of special consideration and protection from parents or parent surrogates until they attain full maturity as adults, the amount of this protection should decrease while the amount of their acknowledged and respected autonomy increases. In its final statement, after receiving many opinions from authorities of different kinds and after much thought and deliberation, the commission recognized the fact of developing autonomy in children by declaring that "children who are seven years of age or older are generally capable of understanding the procedures and general purposes of research and of indicating their wishes regarding participation" (1977, p. 16). Obviously, there might be different views of the correctness of this declaration; the psychological and sociological evidence on the moral development of children is hardly so large that there is full consensus on just when they are capable of participation in informed consent. Still the commission's decision is not unreasonable in the light of what evidence we do have. Enlarging upon its insistence on the importance of personhood for children, the commission has made a distinction between "assent" and "permission" in the process of gaining informed consent that makes explicit the fact of development in children's capacity for moral autonomy. Informed consent must be a mixture of different amounts of "assent" from the child, depending upon his maturing moral capacities, and of "permission" from the parent. There should be more "assent" from the age of seven on and less permission. When we look at the commission's recommendations in detail, we shall see some important specifications and qualifications it made to realize this distinction and fulfill the value of personhood.

This is not the only value involved in research on children. Clearly it also involves the values concerned with their health and welfare and the ways in which these are served by the values we put on science and research. A difficult question arising when these values are acknowledged is whether nontherapeutic research on children is as justified as directly therapeutic research. That is, is it ethically justifiable to use particular children in research that cannot possibly be of direct therapeutic benefit to them for the diseases from which they are suffering as patients? Moral philosophers who have given special attention to bioethics have taken different views of this matter. On one side is the philosopher Paul Ramsey, who has been perhaps the strongest proponent of the value of personhood in all bioethical problems. In his book, significantly entitled *The Patient as a Person,* Ramsey declares that, because of the overriding importance of the value of personhood in contrast to the value of research, nontherapeutic research is never justified (1970). On the other side, for a variety of ethical reasons other moral philosophers have found nontherapeutic research on children acceptable. Some hold that we all, children included, have a general ethical obligation to help others; others argue that the "reasonable" child would want to help others, though it is not clear to different people what is "reasonable" for different children; still others feel that from a certain age children's moral education can profit from participation in research; and finally, in a variation of the "beneficial consequences" position, in ethics, some have held that participation in nontherapeutic research is justified by the good consequences such research can have for children as a class. (For a more detailed statement of these positions, see National Commission, 1977, Chap. 8, and various papers in the Appendix volume. See also Beecher, 1969, p. 82 ff.; and Curran and Beecher, 1969.)

One last important issue in discussions of a policy for using children in research is the value we put upon the maintenance and support of harmonious and integrated families. While both the autonomy of the child and his health and welfare must be recognized, so also must his obligation to contribute to, or not subvert, the effective function of his family. Too much recognition of a child's autonomy or welfare could reduce either the necessary authority of the parents or the welfare of siblings. As is always the case with collectivities and their individual members, the family as a collectivity and the child as an individual may conflict in their values and interests in some situations. A good policy for using children as research subjects must include a recognition of the value of the family.

Because the problem of using children in research is a newly emergent social problem, it is not surprising to discover that changing values are to the fore and that the law that expresses and establishes values still lags somewhat behind the new values or, rather, the new emphases on old values (Capron, 1972).

Until recently, the basic doctrine of common law held that children are chattels of their parents or, parents lacking, wards of the state. Currently, however, as a result of the children's rights movement, there is a considerable trend toward the expansion of children's rights to self-determination and their protection from the sometimes overbearing authority of both parents and the state. There is no longer an established presumption that parents and society always act in the best interests of the child. While this expansion of children's rights to self-determination has taken place with regard to problems of therapeutic treatment in medicine, there is still almost nothing in the decisions of our common law courts with regard to the treatment of children as subjects in research. We have seen earlier that this is also true for adults. As with adults, the new values have been expressed sooner in ethical codes and statutory law than in common law. As to the ethical codes, while the Nuremberg Code did not mention children explicitly, it did require that all subjects have the legal capacity to consent; and this implicitly made children a special case. Later codes have been more explicit about children, as have been the regulations of the Department of Health, Education, and Welfare. It is because the common law is still so silent about children in research, that the national commission has defined *children* as those "who have not attained the legal age of consent to *general medical care*" (1977, p. 3; emphasis added). The commission so acted on the assumption that the rights and protections the common law has given to children with regard to general medical care were the same as those that probably would be given them in cases and decisions involving biomedical research.

It is important therefore to see what the law says about medical treatment of children. In most states, the law still holds that parental consent is both necessary and sufficient for the treatment of persons under eighteen years of age. However, to this general rule there are at least three exceptions. First, when there is an emergency—a condition in which the child's life is threatened or there can be serious bodily harm unless immediate action is taken—and the parents are absent, others may act for the child. Second, the courts have defined as "emancipated minors" persons under eighteen who are married or maintaining their own residences or managing their own finances. These emancipated minors can give legally valid con-

sent to medical treatment. Third, where minors are not emancipated in this legal sense but are still able to comprehend the
treatment offered them, the "mature minor" rule has been
upheld. This rule often applies in situations where it seems desirable that children have the right to self-determination even
though they are not legally emancipated from their families. One
such situation is the treatment of venereal disease; another is
obtaining contraceptive knowledge and devices or even abor-
tions. In these two conditions—emergency and existing capacity for self-determination—the courts have established principles that they would probably also follow in problems of consent
in the research situation. In such problems, the courts might
also borrow precedents not from themselves directly but from
the way in which these precedent principles have been enun-
ciated and codified by such bodies as the national commission
or by such regulatory agencies as the Department of Health,
Education, and Welfare. Still there is an overwhelming tradition
in common law to build directly upon its own principles and
precedents. One large question, of course, is whether the courts
would generalize their decisions about the rights of minors to
consent to therapeutic treatment to the problem of nontherapeutic research. It seems likely that they would; but in the
absence of actual cases, this remains to be discovered. The only
kind of case that seems relevant to this problem is that in which
the courts have allowed minor children to donate kidneys to
their siblings. Although such donations are obviously of no
bodily benefit to the donors, some courts have required some
sort of "proof" (often from psychiatrists) of psychological benefit; other courts have allowed donations even without consideration of benefit to the donor. These cases show that the courts
are not entirely averse to using benefits to others as justification
for consent to treatment or research. But, as Annas and his
colleagues conclude in their summary of the legal issues on the
use of children in consent, "courts will closely scrutinize the
facts of a particular situation to ensure that one who is not capable of protecting his own interests is not being exploited
(Annas, Glantz, and Katz, 1977, p. 50).

Who might be exploiting children in research? What unjus-
tified power, what duress are they subject to? All the conditions
that lead to the authoritarian treatment of adults by physicians
and researchers described in Chapter 4 also obtain for children

as research subjects, even when not only their own assent but also their parents' permission is obtained. Beyond this general possibility for the abuse of power, the national commission has expressed special concern that children not be subject to coercion from either their physicians or their parents. The institutional review boards, the commission has recommended:

> should assure that children who will be asked to participate in research . . . are those with good relationships with their parents or guardians and their physician, and who are receiving care in supportive surroundings. . . . The IRB may wish to appoint someone to assist in the selection of subjects and to review the quality of interaction between parents or guardian and child. A member of the board or a consultant such as the child's pediatrician, a psychologist, a social worker, a pediatric nurse, or other experienced and perceptive person would be appropriate. The IRB should be particularly sensitive to the difficulties surrounding permission when the investigator is the treating physician to whom the parents or guardian may feel an obligation (1977, p. 15).

Not all of these child advocates, not even a child's own pediatrician, are necessarily able to withstand the superior power of the physician investigator. We may remember that in Gray's study of informed consent among women serving as subjects in a test of a new drug for inducing labor several of the poorly informed women were recommended to the study by their own obstetrician. We may also remember that paramedicals like nurses, social workers, and psychologists may be dominated by the physician in charge (Gray, 1975a). Nonetheless, in principle the commission's safeguard is useful. The commission's warning against the possible misuse of power by parents or guardians clearly comes from its awareness of some cases of parental neglect or abuse. In addition, in the case of emancipated or mature minors, parental control may take the form more of powerful coercion than of legitimate and accepted authority.

As we have seen in the case of prisoners, the Michigan Survey Research Center's study for the commission provides us with useful information (Tannenbaum and Cooke, 1977). Written and/or oral consent was used in most but not all biomedical research on children reported in their sample of institutions.

Consent was obtained not only by the investigator himself or someone else on the study staff but also sometimes by nurses, interns, students, or research assistants. Unfortunately, these consent forms were often incomplete in terms of the six consent elements specified in the DHEW regulations for appropriate consent—the purpose of the research, the procedures involved, the risks, the benefits, a statement that subjects are free to withdraw from the research, and an invitation to ask questions. Using a "completeness index" based on these six elements, Tannenbaum and Cooke found that only 20 percent of the forms from children's hospitals and other biomedical institutions were "complete or nearly so." Mention of freedom to withdraw and an invitation to ask questions are most seldom used. The mention of the possibility of alternative treatments also occurs "only rarely." Finally, "words indicating the fact" that the studies were "experimental" also occur "infrequently." As with consent forms in general, when measured on the Flesch Readability Index, the forms examined by Tannenbaum and Cooke were found "generally difficult to read." There is obviously considerable room for improvement on the communication side of gaining informed consent for research on children.

These defects in communication occurred despite the fact that all of the research protocols were approved by institutional review boards whose most common actions had to do with informed consent provisions. About one-fourth of the investigators in the Tannenbaum and Cooke survey said their IRBs had requested changes in the way informed consent should be obtained. Almost all these suggestions pertained to the content of the forms, but this content remained unsatisfactory. It is not surprising therefore that the national commission has recommended some control mechanisms for the consent process beyond that of the IRB. For example, the commission has recommended first, that the solicitation of assent and permission from children and parents be monitored by outsiders and second, that when the IRBs cannot determine whether some piece of proposed research meets the conditions stipulated by the commission there be further control mechanisms in the form of a national ethical advisory board and the secretary of the responsible (funding or sponsoring) department of the government. While the IRBs are an important institutional control innovation, their actual functioning and efficacy, as we have seen earlier, leaves room for improvement.

As is the case with the general population and with prisoners, the problem of constructing a satisfactory policy for the use of children in research requires a difficult balance or adjustment among different but appealing values. The national commission, in its recommendations for such a policy for children, acknowledged and directly confronted this fact (1977, pp. 1–20, 136 ff.). While the commission recognized what it called the values of "beneficence" (the matter of a balance between risks and benefits for the subjects themselves) and of "justice" (the matter of a balance of risks and benefits between the subjects themselves and other social groups that might serve as subjects), it gave primary weight to the value of "respect for personhood." As the commission put it, "the central point of contention in the debate over the ethics of research involving children is the question of consent," a question that arises out of concern for the proper respect for the personhood of children (p. 141). The conditions stipulated by the commission for the protection of this personhood protect the child from infancy to the beginning of adulthood, at first by requiring permission for research from the parents and then, at age seven, when the commission defined the child as morally mature enough to participate in decisions about volunteering, by requiring the assent of the child as well as the permission of the parents. So great is the value put upon the autonomy of the child that the commission declared "the objection of a child to an intervention imposed for research purposes alone should generally be binding. In so doing, it permits the child to protect itself from unpleasant experiences and respects the maturing autonomy of the child" (p. 142). While seeking to prevent unnecessary harm to the integration of the child's family as a collectivity, even in this situation the commission leaned at least ever so slightly to the primacy of the principle of respect for the personhood of the child. We see again, through considering the problem of children as research subjects, that this is the central value for the problem of informed consent in all spheres.

THE MENTALLY INFIRM AND INFORMED CONSENT

Since the problems, processes, and ethical issues involved in obtaining informed consent from the mentally infirm when they are used as research subjects are similar in many important respects to those for prisoners and children, we can be relatively brief in our discussion of this captive and controlled group. As was the case for prisoners and children, when the Congress set up the National Commission for the Protection of Human Subjects, it gave a special mandate to inquire into this especially vulnerable population. As Annas and his colleagues have put it in comparing the mentally infirm to prisoners and children: "The area of informed consent by institutionalized mental patients to experimentation combines the issues found in regard to prisoners and children. The problem is two-tiered, concerning both the legal capacity of the individual to consent and the issue of institutionalization" (Annas, Glantz, and Katz, 1978, p. 1).

The term *mentally infirm,* we should note immediately, comes from lay language and is not a clinical definition in medicine. It is a comprehensive, almost a catchall term used by the Congress to cover a broad range of quite different clinical entities, from relatively mild psychological disturbance to permanent and severe mental retardation. Because the kind of mental disability—from mild to severe, transient to permanent, cognitive to moral—has a great bearing on the degree of competence of any mentally infirm person institutionalized and available for use as a research subject, the commission took pains to emphasize the heterogeneity of this category: "Thus, the term 'mentally infirm' was apparently intended [by Congress] to encompass a broad array of people who, because of cognitive or emotional handicaps, reside in institutions and are subject to institutional constraints." The commission points out that there "is no reference to it in the *Diagnostic and Statistical Manual of Mental Disorders* published by the American Psychiatric Association" (1978a, p. xvii). Finally, the commission makes it clear that by the phrase, "reside in institutions," in its definitional statement it means, again very comprehensively, to include "residents, either by voluntary admission or involuntary commitment, in public or private mental hospitals, psychiatric wards of general hospitals, community mental health centers, half-way houses or nursing homes for the mentally disabled, and similar institutions" (1978a, p. xviii).

Data on the extent to which the mentally infirm are used as research subjects are sparse, but we have some statistics that indicate the order of magnitude of the problem. First, how many institutionalized mentally infirm are there as the pool of potential subjects? In 1973, inpatient psychiatric facilities cared for 1,679,608 "psychiatric episodes," largely among people between the ages of eighteen and sixty-four (National Commission, 1978a, p. 24). Approximately two hundred thousand people reside in 176 public institutions specifically designed for the care of the retarded, and there are another twenty-eight thousand in 1031 private facilities. These are generally the most severely retarded and permanent patients. In addition, thirty thousand mildly and moderately retarded persons reside in state mental hospitals (p. 26). A large number of mentally infirm exist in our society. Moreover, it is estimated that "more than twenty million family members are directly involved with retarded persons" (p. 25).

Not all of the mentally infirm are actually used as subjects. In the national sample survey of institutions having IRBs for the review of research using human subjects which the Survey Research Center of the University of Michigan did for the national commission, it was found that 11 percent of all the research projects that passed through the review boards of the sixty-one institutions in the sample, between July 1974 and June 1975, involved the mentally infirm as subjects. Only about a third of these projects were biomedical, the remainder being primarily behavioral research, though so far as the mentally infirm are concerned these are overlapping categories (Tannenbaum and Cooke, 1978, p. 1). In fiscal 1975, one hundred projects out of five hundred supported by the National Institutes of Mental Health in the areas of clinical research, applied research, psychopharmacology, epidemiology, and services development research involved inpatient populations (National Commission, 1978a, p. 36). The total mental retardation research budget of DHEW for 1973 was thirty-one million dollars (p. 37).

As was the case for its discussion of prisoners and children as research subjects, and as is also clearly the case for noncaptive populations, the national commission stressed the need to consider competing values in constructing any desirable policy for informed consent with the mentally infirm. In this area, the three key values the commission discerned in its other deliberations—respect for persons, beneficence, and justice—all made claims for recognition. And as in other areas, the commission gave some greater weight to respect for persons but emphasized the need to balance that value off against the others: "Serious ethical dilemmas are created by the conflicts between and among these three values. Most of the controversial ethical issues involving those institutionalized as mentally infirm could be structured in the form of such dilemmas. The resolution of those dilemmas requires striking a balance among competing ethical obligations" (1978a, p. 64). Such balances do not consist of equal parts of all three values but of mixtures in which respect for persons is given first consideration and weight. (In casting the balance in this way, the commission may have been influenced by the powerful statement on the priority of individual autonomy even among the mentally infirm by Professor Joseph Goldstein of the Yale Law School in his paper prepared specially for the commission (1978, pp. 12–19).

The significance of fundamental values in a policy on informed consent among mentally infirm research subjects is all the more important in the absence of satisfactory definitional guidelines in current law. Two summaries of possibly relevant law were prepared for the commission, one by Professor Annas and colleagues, the other by Professor Goldstein; both concluded that the law still had little guidance to give. Annas concluded, "Case law is meager, and most state legislatures have yet to address themselves to this area; yet the issues are important" (Annas, Glantz, and Katz, 1978, p. 67). Goldstein concluded, "Overall it is apparent that the current state of the law and scholarly commentary concerning informed consent by the institutionalized mentally infirm to be research subjects is *unsettled and unsettling*. Given this conclusion, a real opportunity to formulate effective policy is presented to the Commission" (1978, p. 9; emphasis added). We shall see in a moment the several recommendations the commission has made to protect the rights of the mentally infirm.

It is of course their weak position, the extent to which power can so easily be exercised over them, that requires that the mentally infirm be protected by the full forces of values, laws, and new social arrangements. We need not rehearse in detail the weakness of the mentally infirm. A summary statement by Annas, Glantz, and Katz prefatory to their review of the relevant law covers the matter briefly:

> Institutionalized mental patients are perhaps the most isolated and underprivileged members of our society. The human and legal rights of mentally ill and retarded persons have been grossly violated for centuries. The result is that they are often victims of numerous social injustices, including horrible facilities, poor or

nonexistent treatment and education, indiscriminate sterilization, and deprivation of basic legal protections, including the performance of unethical and/or illegal human experimentation (1978, p. 1).

The mentally infirm have too often been used as a captive research population because they are easily manipulated and because they have not been well protected by those who were their legal guardians or by the staffs of the institutions in which they reside. The guardians are at a distance and may not care. Medical researchers on the staffs, or those on the staffs who are the friends and colleagues of medical researchers from other institutions, may let their enthusiasm for research overcome their fiduciary obligations to patients who have diminished or absent competence to look out for themselves.

It might be expected that research subjects among the mentally infirm would be somewhat better protected than those from "free-living" populations because of their own diminished power. The evidence from the Survey Research Center's study of IRBs, however, does not support this expectation (Tannenbaum and Cooke, 1978, Chap. 1, Appendix). The data from the center's study show that communications with mentally infirm research subjects are no better than they are for prisoners, children, or other populations, though perhaps not much worse either. IRBs do not function any better as control mechanisms in institutions for the mentally infirm. The data show that consent forms for the mentally infirm and their legal proxies are incomplete and difficult to read. Although IRBs often request changes in consent forms, these changes appear to be only small and ineffective; and the IRBs do not much concern themselves with the actual process of obtaining informed consent. In a situation where medical researchers and peer review boards should be maintaining the highest standards of ethical concern and practice because of the special weakness of their subjects, the evidence shows only the usual mediocre performance.

Given its fully recognized need to protect the mentally infirm from improper use as research subjects and its awareness of present defects in the way the mentally infirm are in fact used, the National Commission concluded its investigations and deliberations by recommending a policy for informed consent for this population that tries to achieve several goals (1978a, Chap. 10). First, and most generally, the policy seeks to balance respect for persons, beneficence, and justice, giving primary weight to the first of these fundamental values. Second, and more specifically, it tries to take into account the different levels of competence present in mentally infirm populations and to give as much autonomy as possible to the different types:

> One primary consideration must be borne in mind: the class of people identified in the Commission's mandate as the 'institutionalized mentally infirm' is not homogeneous. . . . Some members of the class under consideration are clearly competent, both functionally and in the legal sense, to make decisions regarding their participation in research. Others clearly are not. In addition, some patients retain a constant level of competency (or lack thereof) while others may fluctuate with respect to their capacity to understand information, to respond to the real world, or to communicate choices (1978a, p. 114).

Finally, by distinguishing between different amounts of benefit and risk to the mentally infirm serving as research subjects, the commission seeks to set up social control mechanisms of varying degrees of stringency and effectiveness for the protection of these subjects.

In brief summary, the commission's recommendations, made in pursuit of these several goals, state the following:

1. There should be a whole set of general protective conditions for *all* research on the mentally infirm, conditions of the kind required for research on any and all populations of research subjects, whether free-living, prisoners, children, or the mentally infirm. This set of conditions is what the commission calls "the general standard for informed consent," a standard that transcends the particularities of risk–benefit, competency, institutionalization, and age.
2. For research on the mentally infirm where there is *minimal risk that may or may not be of direct benefit*, the subject must consent if he is competent. If not fully so, and the research is relevant to his condition, he must assent to participation or at least not object. If the subject objects to research that is of direct benefit to him, the research may nevertheless be carried out if his participation is explicitly authorized by a court of competent jurisdiction. In addition, as a protection which is in this case at the discretion of the IRB, the IRB may appoint a "consent auditor to ob-

serve the consent process and determine whether each subject (I) consents, or (II) is incapable of consenting and either assents or does not object, or (III) objects to participation" (1978a, p. 8). The commission uses the term *assent* "to describe authorization by a person whose capacity to understand and judge is somewhat impaired by illness or institutionalization, but who remains functional. The standard for 'assent' requires that the subject know what procedures will be performed in the research, choose freely to undergo those procedures, communicate this choice unambiguously, and be aware that subjects may withdraw from participation. This standard is intended to require a lesser degree of comprehension by the subject than would generally support informed consent" (pp. 9–10).

3. For research where there is *more than minimal risk but which is of direct and "fairly immediate" benefit to the mentally infirm research subject,* the same conditions apply, but in addition the "permission" of a guardian is required, and particularly so if the person has been declared mentally incompetent by a court of law. "No official serving in an institutional capacity," however, may serve as guardian in these situations. Here again, it is within the discretion of the IRB to appoint a consent auditor, but in this case the auditor may not only witness the obtaining of assent but also "observe the conduct of research after a subject has assented in order to determine whether the subject continues to assent. The auditor should be responsible only to the Institutional Review Board with respect to such determination and should not be involved (except in the capacity of consent auditor) with the research for which subjects are being sought. The auditor should be a person who is familiar with the physical, psychological, and social needs of the class of prospective subjects, as well as their legal status" (pp. 15–16).

4. For research where there is *more than minimal risk and where it is of no direct benefit to the subject but is "of vital importance for the understanding or amelioration of the type of disorder or condition of the subjects, or (II) may reasonably be expected to benefit the subjects in the future,"* all the above conditions of protection (assent, guardian permission, consent auditor) are required, but in this

case it is mandatory, not discretionary, for the IRB to appoint a consent auditor (p. 11).

5. Finally, any research that does not fall under the conditions stipulated above but "presents an opportunity to understand, prevent, or alleviate a serious problem affecting the health or welfare of persons institutionalized as mentally infirm," must be sent for approval to "a national ethical advisory board and, following opportunity for public review and comment, to the head of the responsible federal department or agency" (p. 20). The commission emphasizes the importance of congressional notification of such research and of "debate in a public forum. . . . Only research of major significance, in the presence of a serious health problem, would justify the approval of research under Recommendation (5). The problem addressed must be a grave one, there must be a reasonable expectation to developing needed scientific information, and an equitable method should be used for selecting subjects who will be invited to participate" (p. 21).

Stipulations such as these, if properly carried out—and we have seen that such is not always the case—would make an effective policy for informed consent in situations where the mentally infirm make desirable research subjects. Although it gives full acknowledgement to the autonomy of the individual, it also recognizes the values of beneficence and justice. Research should still be able to flourish under these conditions.

8

Themes
and
Social Contexts

In conclusion, we can be relatively brief, recalling some of our main themes and referring again to some of the important social contexts in which it is essential to see the social problem of informed consent in medical therapy and research. We have examined many details; it will be useful here at the end to remind ourselves of the larger themes and purposes they illustrate and substantiate.

One of our main purposes has been to show the need for a multidimensional or multivariate conceptual scheme for the analysis of the complex reality of informed consent. Too much thinking about informed consent is simplistic, overemphasizing or making absolute one aspect of a many-sided phenomenon. Our conceptual scheme is multidimensional not for its own sake, not merely as an exercise in abstract social analysis, but because that is what the reality of informed consent processes actually requires if we are to achieve the kind of understanding we need for better social policy. Another of our main purposes, of course, has been to make a contribution to better social policy, to guide physicians, patients and subjects, and government officials in their search to find a more satisfactory balance among their common and diverse values and interests. In this attempt, there is ample scope for common purpose and rational remedy rather than social and political conflict.

As we have illustrated the usefulness of our multidimensional conceptual scheme and presented as much empirical data as we could find about the actual processes of informed consent, one strong theme has appeared: there are many shortcomings in the present arrangements for informed consent in medical relationships. In the light of some of our fundamental social and moral values, there is a need for improvement in all the dimensions of informed consent we have discussed. We need better statutory and case law to guide patients, physicians, and researchers in their encounters with one another. We need some redress of the balance of authority and power among those who participate in the medical system, as all of us eventually do. We urgently need better reciprocal communication between doctors and their patients and subjects. We need to introduce better ethical training for physicians and researchers and make sure that it will constantly respond to change, since the ethical problems of medicine are as dynamic as the scientific and clinical problems. Now that "Continuing Medical Education (CME)" is an institutionalized and flourishing part of the physician's world, it should be revised to include the serious consideration of recurring and emerging ethical dilemmas. We need more effective self-regulation by physicians and researchers and better cooperation in ethical decision making between them and lay participants in the medical system. Finally, we need to pay special attention to special populations of patients and subjects—children, prisoners, and the mentally infirm—whose problems with informed consent are much like those of regular patients but different in some important ways. As we construct special arrangements for these special populations, we can learn better how to deal with regular populations.

We should nevertheless not be blinded by this strong theme of present shortcomings in all aspects of informed consent to another theme our discussion has revealed: the considerable progress and improvement, during the last twenty or twenty-five years, in the processes and practices of informed consent. Reformers should not ignore the progress achieved any more than physicians and researchers, reacting defensively to continuing criticism and calls for still more reform, should not be proud of what has been accomplished. There is a new world of informed consent in medical relationships, a better world than formerly existed even if it still is not so good as it might be. Awareness or consciousness of our problems has been voiced on all sides, and it is a prelude to effective efforts for continuing improvement. The establishment of the institutional review boards by the Department of Health, Education, and Welfare is a considerable achievement, a social invention of the first importance for better ethical standards in the medical system. The reports and recommendations of the National Commission for the Protection of the Human Subjects of Biomedical and Behavioral Research represent a powerful voice for moral and rational remedy in this area, an influence for forestalling and preventing social conflict. In the past twenty years, what the political scientists analyzing the requirements of effective democratic process in our society call an "attentive public," has grown from almost nothing—a whole set of knowledgeable and concerned laymen, physicians, philosophers, lawyers, sociologists, and political scientists who see to it that our concern with improving informed consent is maintained and based increasingly on a high level of moral-philosophical and social analysis and fact.

Further momentum is related to some important features of the social context in which any progress will have to be made. Relatively brief discussion of some of these features will be helpful.

CONTROL AND RESPONSIBILITY IN THE POWERFUL PROFESSIONS

Biomedical science is only one of the many kinds of powerful knowledge without which our society could not operate as it is presently constituted. We also depend on the knowledge exercised by lawyers, accountants, engineers, and a variety of academic scientists and other specialists. Those who are trained in and exercise such powerful knowledge we call *professionals;* and in a sense, our society is as much professional as it is capitalist or industrial. As we saw in Chapter 4, where we discussed the authority and power of physicians and medical researchers, to some extent such special and powerful knowledge is so esoteric that control over its use can be wielded only by those who possess it. To justify their special powers, the professions make two claims: first that they will use their power in the public interest, and second that they will maintain effective self-regulation against abuses of the power.

At the present time, there is widespread public opinion and sentiment that there are defects in all the powerful professions, that they are not satisfactorily displaying public responsibility or maintaining effective self-regulation. (For detailed evidence, see Barber, 1978–1979.) These complaints do not necessarily mean that professions are not performing so well as they once did. They may mean only that people are now more aware than ever before of professional power and that they have developed higher standards of professional responsibility and self-regulation. Whatever the case, the dissatisfaction with the professions is there. Public opinion poll evidence shows that it is not so large as dissatisfaction with two other powerful groups, government and business, but its existence indicates a desire for reform (Lipset and Schneider, 1978).

Although they have their own special characteristics and causes, present complaints against the medical profession with respect to informed consent and other unsatisfactory practices must be seen in this larger social context. All the professions are being asked to do better. The medical profession is not a unique object of criticism.

SOME RECURRING MEDICAL AND SOCIAL DILEMMAS

Certain recurring medical and social dilemmas are also important parts of the social context in which progress in the reform of informed consent practices will be made. First is the *medical dilemma of "caring" as opposed to impersonal technical expertise.* One common complaint against present medical care is that it has become too impersonal, too technical, not compassionate enough, lacking the element of "caring" by the physician for his patient that fosters satisfactory treatment of the patient and his concerns (Lally and Barber, 1974). It is not entirely clear just what "caring" is or should be in medical treatment. Certainly, to some extent medical attention has shifted away from the social and psychological aspects of the patient's concerns to his or her biological structures and processes; this is one consequence of the powerful scientific knowledge and technology now available to the doctor. Caring seems to have to do with the patient's social and psychological concerns, with the "whole person"—as it is sometimes put even in medical school catalogs. Whatever its several and diverse meanings in concrete terms, caring seems to have to do with informed consent. In satisfactory processes of informed consent, the physician or researcher displays a respect and concern for the autonomy and personhood of the patient or subject. Such processes are bound to contribute in some measure to the patient's feeling that the doctor cares for all his essential concerns. Improvement in processes of informed consent would thus seem likely to reduce present widespread feelings that there is not enough caring in medical and research practice.

The *dilemma of authority and equality,* which we discussed in Chapter 4 and to which we have referred earlier in this chapter, is another part of the social context in which the problem of informed consent will work itself out. The special and powerful position their knowledge gives to physicians and researchers is now challenged by the demand, sometimes the overdemand, for greater equality, a powerful countervailing value. The desirable balance between authority and equality is delicate in many social realms, and nowhere more so than in the medical system. The requirement for informed consent from patients and subjects does redress somewhat the present imbalance of authority toward the physician. As further progress in informed consent is proposed, we shall need to be careful that the best balance between authority and equality is carefully considered.

Finally, further reform of informed consent will be involved with the *dilemma*, widespread in our society, *between self-regulation by powerful groups and government control over those groups*. Like other powerful groups, the medical profession resists regulation by government, even when such regulation, as in the case of the N.I.H. requirements beginning in 1966 for local institutional review of informed consent processes, was the only available alternative to the lack of self-regulation by the profession itself. Still, even with considerably improved

professional self-regulation, it is inevitable that some governmental regulation will persist: to define larger social goals
for the professions, to maintain orderly relationships among
competing interests and groups, and to be a court of last
resort for abuses the professions cannot control themselves. As
the virtues of the National Commission for the Protection of
Human Subjects have demonstrated, some kinds of government
regulation can be exceedingly beneficial. It is no more appropriate for physicians and medical researchers to be absolutely
opposed to some government regulation of informed consent
process than it is for businessmen to say that the regulation of
unfair trade practices would lead to the death of business. The
professions will have to live in a world where self-regulation and
government regulation both exist. They can have somewhat less
of the latter if they will themselves create somewhat more of the
former.

MEDICAL ETHICS AND SOCIAL CHANGE

Informed consent is just one part of medical ethics, all of
which just now is in a period of great change (Barber, ed., 1978).
Progress in informed consent processes will be connected with
changes in other problems of medical ethics: abortion, genetic
counseling, and treatment of the dying. Because of the great
biomedical discoveries that are being made and because of the
"egalitarian revolution" in morality that demands better treatment from all professionals, this is a special period in the history
of medicine and medical ethics. Change is inevitable and will be
continuing not only for informed consent but for other aspects
of medical morality. As with all social change, it will be resisted;
but for informed consent and medical ethics generally there
seem to be powerful forces—from government, the public, the
new "bioethicists," and from inside medicine too—slowly over-
coming that resistance. We have made progress; and with the
help of better social analysis and data, we will make more in
creating a more satisfactory informed consent.

References

Adams, Margaret. 1973. "Science, Technology, and Some Dilemmas of Advocacy." *Science* 180, 840.

Alfidi, Ralph J. 1971. "Informed Consent—A Study of Patient Reaction." *Journal of the American Medical Association* 216, 1325–1329.

Altman, Lawrence K. 1972. "Auto-Experimentation." *New England Journal of Medicine* (February 17), 346.

American Correctional Association. 1976. "Position Statement—The American Correctional Association. The Use of Prisoners and Detainees as Subjects of Human Experimentation." Officially adopted February 20, 1976 (in *Prison Inmates in Medical Research,* Hearings before the Subcommittee on Courts . . . on H.R. 3603, p. 612).

Annas, George J. 1978. "Who to Call When the Doctor is Sick," *Hastings Center Report* 8(8), 18–20.

Annas, George J.; Glantz, Leonard H.; and Katz, Barbara F. 1976. "The Law of Informed Consent in Human Experimentation: Prisoners." In National Commission for the Protection of Human Subjects, *Prisoners.*

———. 1977. "Law of Informed Consent in Human Experimentation: Children." In National Commission for the Protection of Human Subjects, *Children.*

———. 1978. "Law of Informed Consent in Human Experimentation: Institutionalized Mentally Infirm." In National Commission for the Protection of Human Subjects, *Institutionalized Mentally Infirm.*

Annas, George J., and Healey, Joseph M., Jr. 1974. "The Patient Rights

Advocate: Redefining the Doctor–Patient Relationship in the Hospital Context." *Vanderbilt Law Review* 27(2), 243–269.

Arnold, John D. 1976. "Alternatives to the Use of Prisoners in Research in the United States." In National Commission for the Protection of Human Subjects, *Prisoners.*

Arnold, John D.; Martin, Daniel C.; and Boyer, Sarah E. 1970. "A Study of One Prison Population and Its Response to Medical Research." In *New Dimensions in Legal and Ethical Concepts for Human Research,* ed. Irving J. Ladimer. *Annals of the New York Academy of Sciences* 168, Art. 2, 463–470.

Aroskar, Mila, and Veatch, Robert M. 1977. "Ethics Teaching in Nursing Schools." *Hastings Center Report* 7(4), 23–26.

Auerbach, Jerold S. 1976. *Unequal Justice: Lawyers and Social Change in Modern America.* New York: Oxford University Press.

Ayd, Frank J., Jr. 1972. "Drug Studies in Prisoner Volunteers," *Southern Medical Journal* 65(4), 440–444.

———. 1973. "Prisoner Volunteers for Medical Research: Motivations and Rewards," *The Medical-Moral Newsletter* 9(7–8), 1–12.

Ayd, Frank J., Jr., and Blackwell, Barry, eds. 1971. "The Scientific and Ethical Problems of Psychotropic Drug Research on Prison Volunteers: A Consensus Communication." *Psychopharmacology Bulletin* (October), 35–38.

Barber, Bernard. 1973. "Research on Human Subjects: Problems of Access to a Powerful Profession." *Social Problems* 21, 103–112.

———. 1976. "Compassion in Medicine: Toward New Definitions and New Institutions." *New England Journal of Medicine* 295, 939–943.

———. 1978–1979. "Control and Responsibility in the Powerful Professions." *Political Science Quarterly* 93, 599–615.

Barber, Bernard, ed. 1978. *Medical Ethics and Social Change. Annals of the American Academy of Political and Social Science* 437 (May).

Barber, Bernard; Lally, John J.; Makarushka, Julia Loughlin; and Sullivan, Daniel. 1973. *Research on Human Subjects: Problems of Social Control in Medical Experimentation.* New York: Russell Sage Foundation.

Bart, Pauline B. 1968. "Social Structure and Vocabularies of Discomfort: What Happened to Female Hysteria?" *Journal of Health and Social Behavior* 9, 188–193.

Baumrind, Diana. 1978. "Nature and Definition of Informed Consent in Research Involving Deception." In National Commission, *Belmont Report.*

Beecher, Henry K. 1966. "Some Guiding Principles for Clinical Investigation." *Journal of the American Medical Association* 195, 1135–1136.

———. 1968. "Medical Research and the Individual." In *Life or Death: Ethics and Options*, ed. Daniel H. Labby. Seattle: University of Washington Press.

———. 1969. "Scarce Resources and Medical Advancement." In *Ethical Aspects of Experimentation with Human Subjects*, ed. Stephen R. Graubard. *Daedalus* 98(2).

———. 1970. *Research and the Individual: Human Studies.* Boston: Little, Brown.

Bergen, Richard P. 1974. "The Confusing Law of Informed Consent." *Journal of the American Medical Association* 229, 325.

Berger, Morroe. 1952. *Equality by Statute: Legal Controls over Group Discrimination.* New York: Columbia University Press.

Berkowitz, Leonard. 1978. "Some Complexities and Uncertainties Regarding the Ethicality of Deception in Research with Human Subjects." In National Commission for the Protection of Human Subjects, *Belmont Report.*

Berlant, Jeffrey L. 1975. *Profession and Monopoly: A Study of Medicine in the United States and Great Britain.* Berkeley and Los Angeles: University of California Press.

Bird, Brian. 1973. *Talking with Patients*, 2nd ed. Philadelphia: J. B. Lippincott.

Blacher, Richard S., and Levine, Herbert J. 1976. "The Language of the Heart." *Journal of the American Medical Association* 236, 1699.

Blackwell, Barry. 1973. "Patient Compliance." *New England Journal of Medicine* 289, 249–252.

Blumgart, Herrman L. 1969. "The Medical Framework for Viewing the Problem of Human Experimentation." In *Ethical Aspects of Experimentation with Human Subjects,* ed. Stephen R. Graubard. *Daedalus* 98(2).

Boyle, C. M. 1970. "Difference between Patients' and Doctors' Interpretation of Some Common Medical Terms." *British Medical Journal* 2, 286–289.

Brandt, Allan M. 1978. "Racism and Research: The Case of the Tuskegee Syphilis Study." *Hastings Center Report* 8(8), 21–29.

Branson, Roy. 1976. "Philosophical Perspectives on Experimentation with Prisoners," In National Commission for the Protection of Human Subjects, *Prisoners.*

———. 1977. "Prison Research: National Commission Says 'No, Unless . . .' " *Hastings Center Report* 7(1), 15–21.

Brant, Charles S., and Kutner, Bernard. 1957. "Physician–Patient Relations in a Teaching Hospital." *Journal of Medical Education* 32, 703–706.

Brody, Howard. 1976. "The 'Patient Package Insert.' " *Journal of the American Medical Association* 235, 1003–1004.

Burt, Robert A. 1977. "The Limits of the Law on Regulating Health Care Decisions." *Hastings Center Report* 7(6), 29–32.

Capron, Alexander Morgan. 1972. "Legal Considerations Affecting Clinical Pharmacological Studies in Children." *Clinical Research* 21, 141–150.

Carlton, Wendy. 1978. *"In Our Professional Opinion . . ."*: The Primacy of Clinical Judgment over Moral Choice. Notre Dame, Indiana: University of Notre Dame Press.

Chalmers, Thomas C. 1969. "A Challenge to Clinical Investigators." *Gastroenterology* 57, 631–635.

Chalmers, Thomas; Block, Jerome; and Lee, Stephanie. 1972. "Controlled Studies in Clinical Cancer Research." *New England Journal of Medicine* 287, 75–78.

Coe, Rodney M.; Pepper, Max; and Wattis, Mary. 1977. "The 'New' Medical Student: Another View." *Journal of Medical Education* 52, 89–98.

Cohen, Carl. 1978. "Medical Experimentation on Prisoners." *Perspectives in Biology and Medicine* 21, 357–372.

Cook, Joyce Mitchell. 1976. "The Problems of Informed Consent, Focussing on Prisons." In National Commission for the Protection of Human Subjects, *Prisoners.*

Cooke, Robert A.; Tannenbaum, Arnold S.; and Gray, Bradford H. 1978. *A Survey of Institutional Review Boards and Research Involving Human Subjects.* Washington, D. C.: U. S. Government Printing Office.

Crane, Diana. 1975. *The Sanctity of Social Life: Physicians' Treatment of Critically Ill Patients.* New York: Russell Sage Foundation.

Crile, George, Jr. 1972. "Breast Cancer and Informed Consent." *Cleveland Clinic Quarterly* 39(2), 57–59.

Curran, William J. 1969. "Governmental Regulation of the Use of Human Subjects in Medical Research: The Approach of Two Federal Agencies." In *Ethical Aspects of Experimentation with Human Subjects,* ed. Stephen R. Graubard. *Daedalus* 98(2).

————. 1974. "The First Mechanical Heart Transplant: Informed Consent and Experimentation." *New England Journal of Medicine* 291, 1015–1016.

Curran, William J., and Beecher, Henry K. 1969. "Experimentation in Children: A Reexamination of Legal Ethical Principles." *Journal of the American Medical Association* 210, 77–83.

Davis, Alan J. 1972. "Sexual Assaults in the Philadelphia Prison System." In *Muckraking Sociology: Research as Social Criticism*, ed. Gary T. Marx. New Brunswick, N. J.: Transaction Books.

Davis, Milton S. 1967. "Predicting Non-Compliant Behavior." *Journal of Health and Social Behavior* 8, 265–271.

————. 1968. "Physiologic, Psychological and Demographic Factors in Patient Compliance with Doctors' Orders." *Medical Care* 11, 115–122.

Derbyshire, Robert C. 1965. "What Should the Profession Do about the Incompetent Physician?" *Journal of the American Medical Association* 194, 1287–1290.

————. 1974. "Medical Ethics and Discipline." *Journal of the American Medical Association* 228, 59–62.

Dimond, E. Gray, M.D. 1974. "The Physician and the Quality of Life."

Journal of the American Medical Association 228, 1117–1119.

Ellis, Rosemary. 1970. "The Nurse as Investigator and Member of the Research Team." In *New Dimensions in Legal and Ethical Concepts for Human Research*, ed. Irving J. Ladimer. *Annals of the New York Academy of Sciences* 168, Art. 2, 435–441.

Epstein, Lynn Chaikin, and Lasagna, Louis. 1969. "Obtaining Informed Consent: Form or Substance." *Archives of Internal Medicine* 123, 682–688.

Etzioni, Amitai, and Nunn, Clyde. 1974. "The Public Appreciation of Science in Contemporary America." *Daedalus* 103, 191–205.

Fellner, Carl H., and Marshall, John R. 1970. "Kidney Donors—The Myth of Informed Consent." *American Journal of Psychiatry* 126, 1245.

Fellner, Carl H., and Schwartz, Shalom H. 1971. "Altruism in Disrepute." *New England Journal of Medicine* 284, 282–285.

Ferguson, Lucy Rau. 1977. "The Competence and Freedom of Children to Make Choices Regarding Participation in Biomedical and Behavioral Research." In National Commission for the Protection of Human Subjects, *Research Involving Children: Report and Recommendations,* Appendix. Washington, D. C.: U. S. Government Printing Office.

Fletcher, John. 1973. "Realities of Patient Consent to Medical Research." *Hastings Center Studies* 1(1), 39–49.

Fost, Norman C. 1975. "A Surrogate System for Informed Consent." *Journal of the American Medical Association* 233, 800–803.

———. 1977. "Children as Renal Donors." *New England Journal of Medicine* 296, 363–367.

Fox, Renée C. 1959. *Experiment Perilous*. Glencoe, Ill.: Free Press.

———. 1976. "Advanced Medical Technology—Social and Ethical Implications." In *Annual Review of Sociology, 1976,* ed. Alex Inkeles et al. Palo Alto, Calif.: Annual Reviews.

Francis, Vida; Korsch, B. M.; and Morris, M. J. 1969. "Gaps in Doctor–Patient Communication: Patients' Response to Medical Advice." *New England Journal of Medicine* 280, 535–540.

Freeman, Barbara; Negrete, V. F.; Davis, M.; and Korsch, B. M. 1971. "Gaps in Doctor–Patient Communication: Doctor–Patient Interaction Analysis." *Pediatric Research* 5, 298–311.

Freidson, Eliot. 1970. *Professional Dominance: The Social Structure of Medical Care*. New York: Atherton.

———. 1974. "Toward a More Open Profession." *PRISM* (March), 41.

Freund, Paul A. 1969. "Legal Frameworks for Human Experimentation." In *Ethical Aspects of Experimentation with Human Subjects*, ed. Stephen R. Graubard. *Daedalus* 98(2).

Fried, Charles. 1974. *Medical Experimentation: Personal Integrity and Social Policy*. Amsterdam: Elsevier.

Garnham, J. C. 1975. "Some Observations on Informed Consent in Non-Therapeutic Research." *Journal of Medical Ethics* 1, 138–145.

Gaylin, Willard; Glasser, Ira; Marcus, Steven; and Rothman, David, eds. 1978. *Doing Good: The Limits of Benevolence.* New York: Pantheon.

Glaser, Barney G., and Strauss, Anselm L. 1965. *Awareness of Dying.* Chicago: Aldine.

Goldstein, Joseph. 1978. "On the Right of the 'Institutionalized Mentally Infirm' to Consent to or Refuse to Participate as Subjects in Biomedical and Behavioral Research." In National Commission for the Protection of Human Subjects, *Institutionalized Mentally Infirm.*

Graubard, Stephen R., ed. 1969. *Ethical Aspects of Experimentation with Human Subjects. Daedalus* 98(2).

————. 1978. *Limits of Scientific Inquiry. Daedalus* (spring).

Gray, Bradford H. 1975a. *Human Subjects in Medical Experimentation.* New York: Wiley-Interscience.

————. 1975b."An Assessment of Institutional Review Committees in Human Experimentation." *Medical Care* 13, 318–328.

Gray, Bradford H.; Cooke, Robert A.; and Tannenbaum, Arnold S. 1978. "Research Involving Human Subjects." *Science* 201, 1094–1101.

Green, R. C.; Carroll, G. J.; and Buxton, W. D. 1978. *The Care and Management of the Sick and Incompetent Physician.* Springfield, Ill.: C. C. Thomas.

Haug, Marie, and Lavin, Bebe. 1978. "Method of Payment for Medical Care and Public Attitudes toward Physician Authority." *Journal of Health and Social Behavior* 19, 279–291.

Headlee, R. 1973. "Peer Review Blues." *Wisconsin Medical Journal* 72, 6–7.

Hirsh, Bernard D. 1970. "The Medicolegal Framework for Clinical Research in Medicine." In *New Dimensions in Legal and Ethical Concepts for Human Research,* ed. Irving J. Ladimer. *Annals of the New York Academy of Sciences* 168, Art. 2, 308–315.

Hodges, Robert E., and Bean, William B. 1967. "The Use of Prisoners for Medical Research." *Journal of the American Medical Association* 202, 177.

Hofling, C. K.; Brotzman, E.; Dalrymple, S.; Graves, N.; and Purce, C. M. 1966. "An Experimental Study in Nurse–Physician Relationships." *Journal of Nervous and Mental Disease* 143(2), 171–180.

Holder, A. R. 1970. "Informed Consent." *Journal of the American Medical Association* 214, 1181–1182.

Holman, E. J. 1973. "Hard Cases Make Bad Law." *Journal of the American Medical Association* 226, 562.

Hulka, Barbara S.; Cassel, John C.; and Kupper, Lawrence L. 1976. "Disparities between Medications Prescribed and Consumed among Chronic Disease Patients." *American Journal of Public Health* (September), 27–45.

Hulka, Barbara S.; Zyzanski, S.; Cassel, John C.; and Thompsom, Shirley. 1970. "Scale for the Measurement of Attitudes toward Physicians and Primary Medical Care." *Medical Care* 8(5), 429.

Illich, Ivan. 1976. *Medical Nemesis: The Expropriation of Health*. New York: Pantheon.

Irwin, John. 1976. "An Acceptable Context for Biomedical Research." In National Commission for the Protection of Human Subjects, *Prisoners*.

Jaffe, Louis L. 1969. "Law as a System of Control." In *Ethical Aspects of Experimentation with Human Subjects,* ed. Stephen R. Graubard. *Daedalus* 98(2).

James, George. 1970. "Clinical Research in Achieving the Right to Health." In *New Dimensions in Legal and Ethical Concepts for Human Research,* ed. Irving J. Ladimer. *Annals of the New York Academy of Sciences* 168, Art. 2, 301–307.

Jameton, Andrew. 1977. "The Nurse: When Roles and Rules Conflict." *Hastings Center Report* 7(4), 22–23.

Jonas, Hans. 1969. "Philosophical Reflections on Experimenting with Human Subjects." In *Ethical Aspects of Experimenting with Human Subjects,* ed. Stephen R. Graubard. *Daedalus* 98(2).

Jonsen, Albert R.; Parker, Michael L.; Carlson, Rick J.; and Emmott, Carol B. 1975. "Biomedical Experimentation on Prisoners: Review of Practices and Problems and Proposal of a New Regulatory Approach." In hearings before the Subcommittee on Courts, Civil Liberties . . . on H.R. 3603, 517–563. Health Policy Program, Faculty of Medicine, University of California, San Francisco, September 1975.

Kahn, Alfred J.; Kamerman, S. B.; and McGowan, B. G. 1972. *Child Advocacy: Report of a National Baseline Study*. New York: Columbia University School of Social Work, Child Advocacy Research Project.

Katz, Jay. 1977. "Informed Consent—A Fairy Tale? Law's Vision." *University of Pittsburgh Law Review* 39, 137–174.

Katz, Jay, ed. 1972. *Experimentation with Human Subjects*. New York: Russell Sage Foundation.

Kimball, C. P. 1971. "Medicine and Dialects." *Annals of Internal Medicine* 74(1), 137–139.

Korsch, Barbara; Gozzi, E. K.; and Francis, V. 1968. "Gaps in Doctor–Patient Communication: 1. Doctor–Patient Interaction and Patient Satisfaction." *Pediatrics* 42, 855–871.

Ladimer, Irving J. 1963. "Clinical Research Insurance." *Journal of Chronic Disease* 16, 1229–1235.

Ladimer, Irving J., ed. 1970. *New Dimensions in Legal and Ethical Concepts for Human Research. Annals of the New York Academy of Sciences* 168, Art. 2, 293–593.

Laforet, Eugene G. 1976. "The Fiction of Informed Consent." *Journal of the American Medical Association* 235, 1579–1585.

Lally, John J. 1978. "The Making of the Compassionate Physician Investigator." In *Medical Ethics and Social Change,* ed. Bernard Barber.

Annals of the American Academy of Political and Social Science 437 (May), 86–98.

Lally, John J., and Barber, Bernard. 1974. " 'The Compassionate Physician': Frequency and Social Determinants of Physician–Investigator Concern for Human Subjects." *Social Forces* 53, 289–296.

Lasagna, Louis. 1973. Editorial, *New England Journal of Medicine* 289, 267–268.

Levine, Robert J. 1978a. "The Role of Assessment of Risk Benefit Criteria in the Determination of the Appropriateness of Research Involving Human Subjects." In National Commission for the Protection of Human Subjects, *The Belmont Report.*

———. 1978b. "The Nature and Definition of Informed Consent in Various Research Settings." In National Commission for the Protection of Human Subjects, *The Belmont Report.*

Lidz, Charles W. 1977. "The Writing on the Form–Informed Consent?" University of Pittsburgh. Mimeo.

Lipsett, Mortimer B.; Fletcher, John C.; and Secundy, Marian. 1978. "Research Review at NIH," *Hastings Center Report* 9(1), 18–21.

Lipset, Seymour Martin, and Schneider, William. 1978. "How's Business? What the Public Thinks." *Public Opinion* 1(3), 41–47.

Martin, Daniel C.; Arnold, John D.; Zimmerman, T. F.; and Richart, Robert H. 1968. "Human Subjects in Clinical Research—A Report of Three Studies." *New England Journal of Medicine* 279, 1426–1431.

Mazzulo, J. M. 1972. "The Nonpharmacologic Basis of Therapeutics." *Clinical Pharmacology and Therapeutics* 13, 157–158.

McCartney, James J. 1978. "Research on Children: National Commission says 'Yes, If . . . .' " *Hastings Center Report* 8(5), 26–31.

McCollum, Audrey T., and Schwartz, A. Herbert. 1969. "Pediatric Research Hospitalization: Its Meaning to Parents." *Pediatric Research* 3, 199–204.

McDonald, J. C. 1967. "Why Prisoners Volunteer to Be Experimental Subjects." *Journal of the American Medical Association* 202, 511–512.

Mead, Margaret. 1969. "Research with Human Beings: A Model Derived from Anthropological Field Practice." In *Ethical Aspects of Experimentation with Human Subjects,* ed. Stephen R. Graubard. *Daedalus* 98(2).

Mechanic, David. 1978. "Ethical Problems in the Delivery of Health Services." In National Commission for the Protection of Human Subjects, *Ethical Guidelines for the Delivery of Health Services by DHEW.*

Mellinger, Glen D. 1976, 1978. "Progress Reports: Public Judgments about Ethical Issues on Research." Berkeley, Calif.: Institute for Research on Social Behavior. Mimeo.

Menges, Robert J. 1973. "Openness and Honesty versus Coercion and

Deception in Psychological Research." *American Psychologist* 28, 1030–1034.

Merton, Robert K. 1978. "Social Problems and Sociological Theory." In *Contemporary Social Problems*, ed. Robert K. Merton and Robert Nisbet. 3rd ed. New York: Harcourt Brace Jovanovich.

Milgram, Stanley. 1974. *Obedience to Authority.* New York: Harper & Row.

Miller, Robert, and Willner, Henry S. 1974. "The Two-Part Consent Form." *New England Journal of Medicine* 290, 966.

Miller, Stephen J. 1970. *Prescription for Leadership.* Chicago: Aldine.

Millman, Marcia. 1977. *The Unkindest Cut: Life in the Backrooms of Medicine.* New York: Morrow.

Mitchell, R. G. 1964. "The Child and Experimental Medicine." *British Medical Journal* 1, 721–727.

Mitford, Jessica. 1974. *Kind and Usual Punishment.* New York: Random House.

Morris, R. Curtis. 1972. "Guidelines for Accepting Volunteers: Consent, Ethical Implications, and the Function of a Peer Review." *Clinical Pharmacology and Therapeutics* 13, 782–786.

National Commission for the Protection of Human Subjects of Biomedical and Behavioral Research. 1976. *Research Involving Prisoners: Report and Recommendations.* 2 vols. Washington, D. C.: U. S. Government Printing Office.

———. 1977. *Research Involving Children: Report and Recommendations.* 2 vols. Washington, D. C.: U. S. Government Printing Office.

———. 1978a. *Research Involving those Institutionalized as Mentally Infirm: Report and Recommendations.* Washington, D. C.: U. S. Government Printing Office.

———. 1978b. *Report and Recommendations: Institutional Review Boards.* Washington, D. C.: U. S. Government Printing Office.

———. 1978c. *The Belmont Report: Ethical Principles and Guidelines for the Protection of Human Subjects of Research.* 3 vols. Washington, D. C.: U. S. Government Printing Office.

———. 1978d. *Report and Recommendations: Ethical Guidelines for the Delivery of Health Services by DHEW.* 2 vols. Washington, D.C.: U. S. Government Printing Office.

———. 1978e. *Special Study: Implications of Advances in Biomedical and Behavioral Research.* Washington, D. C.: U. S. Government Printing Office.

National Immunization Work Groups. 1977. Reports and Recommendations. Washington, D. C.: Office of Assistant Secretary for Health. Mimeo.

Nelson, Benjamin. 1969. *The Idea of Usury: From Tribal Brotherhood to Universal Otherhood.* 2nd ed., enlarged. Chicago: University of Chicago Press.

Note. 1973. "Informed Consent—a Proposed Standard for Medical Disclosure," *New York University Law Review* 48, 548–563.

Park, Lee C.; Covi, Lino; and Uhlenhuth, E. H. 1967. "Effects of Informed Consent on Research Patients and Study Results." *Journal of Nervous and Mental Disease* 145, 349–357.

Park, Lee C.; Slaughter, Regina; Covi, Lino; and Kniffin, Hazen G. 1966. "The Subjective Experience of the Research Patient: An Investigation of Psychiatric Outpatients' Reactions to the Research Treatment Situation." *Journal of Nervous and Mental Disease* 143, 199–206.

Parsons, Talcott. 1939. "The Professions and Social Structure." *Social Forces* 17, 457–467.

———. 1951. *The Social System.* Glencoe, Ill.: Free Press.

———. 1954. *Essays on Sociological Theory.* rev. ed. Glencoe, Ill.: Free Press.

———. 1969. "Research with Human Subjects and the 'Professional Complex.' " In *Ethical Aspects of Experimentation with Human Subjects,* ed. Stephen R. Graubard. *Daedalus* 98(2).

Pellegrino, E. D. 1976. "Medical Ethics, Education and the Physician's Image." *Journal of the American Medical Association* 235, 1043–1044.

Plaut, Thomas F. 1975. "Doctors' Orders and Patient Compliance." *New England Journal of Medicine* 292, 438.

Podell, Richard N., and Gary, Louis R. 1976. "Hypertension and Compliance: Implications for the Primary Physician." *New England Journal of Medicine* 294, 1120–1121.

Pyrczak, Fred. 1978. "Application of Some Principles of Readability Research in the Preparation of Patient Package Inserts." Rochester, N. Y.: University of Rochester Medical Center, The Center for the Study of Drug Development. Mimeo.

Ramsey, Paul. 1970. *The Patient as a Person.* New Haven: Yale University Press.

Rank, Steven G., and Jacobson, Cardell K. 1977. "Hospital Nurses' Compliance with Medication Overdose Orders: A Failure to Replicate." *Journal of Health and Social Behavior* 18, 188–193.

Reich, Warren, ed. 1978. *Encyclopedia of Bioethics.* New York: Free Press.

Robertson, John A. 1978. "Ten Ways to Improve IRBs." *Hastings Center Report* 9(1), 29–33.

Robinson, Daniel N. 1974. "Harm, Offense, and Nuisance: Some First Steps in the Establishment of an Ethics of Treatment." *American Psychologist* 29, 233–238.

Robinson, George, and Merav, Avraham. 1976. "Informed Consent: Recall by Patients Tested Postoperatively." Bronx, N. Y.: Montefiore Hospital and Medical Center. Mimeo.

Rubsamen, David S. 1973. "Changes in 'Informed Consent.' " *Medical World News* (February 9).

Rule, James B. 1978. *Insight and Social Betterment: A Preface to Applied Social Science.* New York: Oxford University Press.

Savard, Robert J. 1970. "Serving Investigator, Patient and Community in Research Studies." In *New Dimensions in Legal and Ethical Concepts for Human Research,* ed. Irving J. Ladimer. *Annals of the New York Academy of Sciences* 168, Art. 2, 429–434.

Schultz, Amelia L., and Pardee, Geraldine P. 1975. "Are Research Subjects Really Informed?" *The Western Journal of Medicine* 123, 76–80.

Schwartz, Doris; Wang, Mamie; Zeitz, Leonard; and Gass, Mary. 1962. "Medication Errors Made by Elderly, Chronically Ill Patients." *American Journal of Public Health* 52, 2018–2029.

Schwartz, William B., and Komesar, Neil K. 1978. "Doctors, Damages and Deterrence: An Economic View of Medical Malpractice." *New England Journal of Medicine* 298, 1282–1289.

Seligmann, Arthur; McGrath, Neva; and Pratt, Doris. 1957. "Level of Medical Information among Clinic Patients." *Journal of Chronic Diseases* 6(5), 497–509.

Shaw, Laurence W., and Chalmers, Thomas C. 1970. "Ethics in Cooperative Clinical Trials." *Annals of the New York Academy of Sciences* 169, 487–495.

Shenkin, Budd N., and Warner, David C. 1973. "Giving the Patient his Medical Record: A Proposal to Improve the System." *New England Journal of Medicine* 289, 688–691.

Shirkey, Harry C. 1972. "Clinical Pharmacology in Therapeutics." *Clinical Pharmacology and Therapeutics* 13, 827–830.

Shuy, Roger W. 1972. "Sociolinguistics and the Medical History." Mimeo. Washington, D. C.: Georgetown University, Department of Linguistics.

———. 1973. "Problems of Communication in the Cross-Cultural Medical Interview." Mimeo. Washington D. C.: Georgetown University, Department of Linguistics.

Shuy, Roger W., and Rubin, Joan. 1973. "Proposal to Investigate the Effect of Stereotyping in the Communication between Doctors and Female Patients." Mimeo. Washington D. C.: Georgetown University, Department of Linguistics.

Simonaitis, Joseph E. 1972. "Recent Decisions on Informed Consent." *Journal of the American Medical Association* 221, 441–442.

———. 1973. "More about Informed Consent." *Journal of the American Medical Association* 224, 831–832.

Smith, Harmon L. 1974. "Myocardial Infarction—Case Studies of Ethics in the Consent Situation." *Social Science and Medicine* 8, 399–404.

Sorenson, James R. 1974. "Biomedical Innovation, Uncertainty, and Doctor–Patient Interaction." *Journal of Health and Social Behavior* 15, 366–374.

Spodick, David H. 1971. "Revascularization of the Heart—Numerators

in Search of Denominators." *American Heart Journal* 81 (2), 149–157.
———. 1973. "The Surgical Mystique and the Double Standard." *American Heart Journal* 85, 579–583.

Steinfels, Margaret O'Brien. 1977. "Ethics, Education, and Nursing Practice." *Hastings Center Report* 7(4), 20–21.

Svarstad, Bonnie L. 1976. "Physician–Patient Communication and Patient Conformity with Medical Advice." In *The Growth of Bureaucratic Medicine,* ed. David Mechanic. New York: John Wiley.

Swazey, J.; Klerman, G.; and Neville, R. 1973. "Regulatory Models for Therapeutic Innovation: Surgery and Drugs." Mimeo. Boston: Harvard Medical School.

Tannenbaum, Arnold S., and Cooke, Robert A. 1976. "Research on Prisons: A Preliminary Report." In National Commission for the Protection of Human Subjects, *Prisoners.*

———. 1977. "Research Involving Children." In National Commission for the Protection of Human Subjects, *Children.*

———. 1978. "Report on the Mentally Infirm." In National Commission for the Protection of Human Subjects, *Institutionalized Mentally Infirm.*

Titmuss, Richard M. 1971. *The Gift Relationship.* New York: Pantheon.

U. S. Department of Health, Education and Welfare. 1971. *The Institutional Guide to DHEW Policy on Protection of Human Subjects.* Washington, D. C.: U. S. Government Printing Office.

U. S. Senate, 93rd Cong. 1st sess. 1973. *Quality of Health Care—Human Experimentation, 1973.* 3 vols. Hearings before the Subcommittee on Health of the Committee on Labor and Public Welfare, February 1–23, March 6–8, 1973. Washington, D. C.: U. S. Government Printing Office.

Vaccarino, James M. 1978. "Consent, Informed Consent and the Consent Form," *New England Journal of Medicine* 298, 455.

Veatch, Robert M. 1978a. "The National Commission on IRBs: An Evolutionary Approach." *Hastings Center Report* 9(1), 22–28.

———. 1978b. "Three Theories of Informed Consent: Philosophical Foundations and Policy Implications." In National Commission for the Protection of Human Subjects, *The Belmont Report.*

Veatch, Robert M., and Sollitto, Sharman. 1976. "Medical Ethics Teaching: Report of a National Medical School Survey." *Journal of the American Medical Association* 235, 1030–1031.

Waltz, Jon R., and Scheuneman, Thomas W. 1969. "Informed Consent to Therapy." *Northwestern University Law Review* 64, 628–650.

Welt, Louis G. 1961. "Reflections on the Problems of Human Experimentation." *Connecticut Medicine* 25, 75–78.

Westin, Alan F. 1967. *Privacy and Freedom.* New York: Atheneum.

———. 1972. *National Academy of Sciences Project on Computer Databanks.* New York: Quadrangle.

————. 1977. "Medical Records: Should Patients Have Access?" *Hastings Center Report* 7(6), 23–28.

Williams, Robin M., Jr. 1971. "Change and Stability in Values and Value Systems." In *Stability and Social Change,* ed. Bernard Barber and Alex Inkeles. Boston: Little, Brown.

Zerubavel, Eviatar. 1977. "The Bureaucratization of Responsibility and Informed Consent." University of Pittsburgh. Mimeo.

Zola, Irving Kenneth. 1972. "Medicine As an Institution of Social Control." *The Sociological Review* 20, 487–504.

Index

Alfidi, Ralph J., 83–84
Altman, Lawrence K., 27
Altruism, 20–21, 80, 160–161
American Hospital Association, 29, 105
American Medical Association: consent principles and, 40; ethics committees and, 149–150; impaired physicians and, 146; individualism and, 23; licensing boards and, 151; prisoner subjects and, 156; professional code of, 28–29. See also *Journal of the American Medical Association*
American Nurses Association, 65, 66
Angiography, 83–84
Animals, research testing and, 157, 168
Annas, George, 106, 146, 161, 174, 178, 180
Antiscientism, 25
Arnold, John D., 156, 157
Authoritarianism: patient's view of, 61–64; of physicians, 50–51; social source of, 74; submissive patients and, 72, 74; as a term, 53
Authority: collegiality model and, 53, 54, 56, 57–58, 60; dilemma of, 189–

Authority (*continued*)
190; doctor/patient, 61–64; dominance model and, 53–61; equality dilemma and, 74–75; in hospitals, 64–69; medical relationships and, 53–61; moral consensus and, 52; patterns in, 61–75; power/professionals and, 188; social source of, 74; social systems/relationships and, 51–53; surgery and, 69–71
Autoexperimentation, 27
Autonomy, 135, 142, 153; child's, 169, 170–171, 172, 177; dominance model and, 58; legal principles and, 32; medical records and, 104; as a medical value, 22–24; mentally infirm and, 180, 184; moral injury and, 3, 5; prisoners, 158
Ayd, Frank, 159–160

Balter, Mitchell, 5
Barber, Bernard, 26–27
Battery/negligence, consent and, 35–36, 44
Beecher, Henry, 23, 26

Benefits: medical records and, 106; probability of, 3. *See also* Risks–benefits ratio

Bergen, Richard P., 39

Beth Israel Hospital, 29

Biological person: injury and, 5; social person and, 3–4

Biomedical research: attitudes toward, 25; autoexperimentation and, 27; children as subjects in, 166–177; codes for, 29–30; colleagues and, 129–133; communication and, 106–115; consent errors and, 6–13; consent form write-up and, 115–119; data/evidence and, 12; deception in, 119–121; dissimulation and, 107; ethical training and, 123–127; evasions in, 109, 111, 114–115; experimental drugs and, 42–43; funds/ethics and, 25; legal outlook and, 45–46; legal principles and, 34–35, 41–45; medical norms/values and, 15; mentally infirm and, 177–184; prisoners used in, 155–166; researcher accessibility and, 86; review boards and, 136–145; risks/benefits and, 110–114; rules of consent and, 108–110; social/moral problems and, 1–6. *See also* Researchers

Bird, Brian, 63, 64

Blackwell, Barry, 93

Blood donation, altruism and, 21

Boyle, C. M., 86–87

Branson, Roy, 160–161, 163

Calvin, John, 21

Canterbury v. *Spence,* 46

Cardiologists: bypass surgery and, 69–70, 120–121; medical terms/patients and, 89–90; risk procedures and, 110–112; surgery/patient's memory and, 82–83

Cardozo, Judge, 36

Caring versus impersonal expertise, 188–190

Carlton, Wendy, 100, 127, 129

Child advocacy, 167–168, 175, 177

Children as research subjects, 166–177

Childrens Hospital of Los Angeles, 87, 100

Cobbs v. *Grant,* 46

Codes. *See* Professional medical codes

Coe, Rodney M., 126–127

Collegiality model of medical relationships, 53, 54, 56, 57–58, 60; Parson's conception of, 54

Communication, 102, 103, 105, 106; Bird's ideas concerning, 64; child subjects and, 176; compliance problems and, 94–95; consent forms and, 117, 119; dominance structure of medical relationships and, 58–59; drug errors and, 96–99; duty of physicians/consent and, 48; fully informed patients and, 83–84; functions/dilemmas of, 77–84; importance of, 76–77; mentally infirm and, 181, 183; patient competence and, 79; perfectionism in, 81–83; physician accessibility and, 85–86; physician/patient, 62; prisoner subjects and, 164, 165; rationality and, 79–81; reasonably informed patients and, 40; research and, 106–115; structures/consent errors and, 8–9; vocabularies of illness and, 86–91

Competence gap, 55, 57

Competence of patient, 78–79

Compliance studies of patients, 91–99

Consent form: children and, 175–176; court ruling on, 45; examples of, 117–119; Gray's study of, 141–143; mentally infirm and, national commission recommendations, 181–184; prisoners and, 164–165, 166; readability of, 114–115, 143, 165, 176; research admission, 113–114; standard, preparing of, 49; surrogate system of, 116–117; tape recorded, 110–111; wording of, 114, 141; writing of, 115–116; as a written document, 48

Consent (informed). *See* Informed consent; *specific aspects of informed consent*

Conspiracy of silence, 38, 133–135

Continuing Medical Education (CME), 186

Controlled trials, 69, 81–82, 120–121
Cook, Joyce M., 161
Cooke, Robert, 114–115, 142, 143, 163, 164, 176
Cooley, Denton A., 43, 48
Curran, William, 41–42, 44, 136, 137

Davis, Milton S., 92, 93, 94, 95
Deception in medical research, 119–121
Dentistry, 58
Department of Health, Education, and Welfare: American Nurses Association and, 66; child development and, 167; children and, 173, 176; consent reform and, 187; harm/consent and, 144–145; mentally infirm and, 179; peer review committees and, 41, 143; policy statement/human research, 44; prisoners and, 162; rules for consent, 108–110, 111
Derbyshire, Robert, 145–147, 149–150, 150–152
Diabetes mellitus, Hulka study and, 95–97
Diamond, E. Gray, 26
Doctors. *See* Physicians
Dominance model of medical relationships, 53–61
Drug Amendments Act of 1962, 42, 137
Drugs, 69; antimalarial, prisoners and, 156; compliance studies and, 92, 94–95; error rates and, 93, 94, 96, 98; experimental, ethical problems and, 128; hallucinogenic, research and, 124; labor-inducing, consent study and, 112–113, 131, 140, 175; new, scandals and, 42–43, 137–138; scale, children and, 168; testing of, consent forms and, 117; testing of, prisoners and, 157

Emancipated minors, 173–174, 175
Emergency situations, 37, 112; children and, 173–174
Epstein, Lynn C., 117–118

Equality, 2, 16, 17, 28; altruism and, 21; authority and, 74–75; as medical dilemma, 189; medical law and, 33; medical norms/values and, 18–20; patient's rights and, 29
Errors, consent and. *See* Human errors
Ethics. *See* Medical ethics; Morality
Ethics committees. *See* Medical Society Ethics Committees
Etzioni, Amitai, 25

Faith. *See* Trust/faith
Family, children as subjects and the, 172, 175
Fears in patients, communication and, 81–82
Federal Bureau of Prisons, 157, 161
Fellner, Carl H., 21, 22, 79, 80
Ferguson, Lucy Rau, 170
Fetuses, 4
Fletcher, John, 5
Food and Drug Administration, 41, 69, 137; drug experiments and, 42–43; ethical review and, 138; testing drugs, prisoners and, 157
Fortner v. *Koch,* 42
Fost, Norman C., 22, 116–117
Fox, Renée C., 54
Freund, Paul A., 21, 32, 56
Freidson, Eliot, 7, 54, 56–60, 65, 132

Gary, Louis R., 95
Genetic counseling, 55, 75
Genetic research, ethical concerns and, 124
Goals, in social systems, 52
Goddard, Commissioner (F.D.A.), 138
Goffman, Erving, 163
Goldberg, B. Abbott, 133
Goldstein, Joseph, 180
Grad, Frank, 40, 49
Gray, Bradford, 112–113, 131, 175; review boards and, 140–143
Green, Governor, 156

Harvard Medical Unit, 128
Heart transplants, 22
Helsinki Declaration, 42, 43
HEW. *See* Department of Health, Education, and Welfare
Hippocratic Oath, 28
Hippocratic writings, compliance and, 91
Hirsh, Bernard D., 40
Hofling, C. K., 67, 68
Hollenberg, kidney donors and, 22
Holman, E. J., 150, 151
Holmes, Justice, 32
Hospital review committees and procedures, 145–149. *See also* Institutional review boards; Peer review committees
Hospitals: bureaucratic segmentation of, 86; medical authority in, 64–69; patients' rights and, 29; patients in, withholding information from, 58–59; review committees in, 145–149
Hulka, Barbara S., 95–97, 100–101
Human errors, consent and: cognitive understanding and, 9; communication, 8–9; impossibility of real consent and, 10–13; individual, 6–7; patients' memory and, 82–83; psychological, 7–8
Human research subjects: altruism and, 21; autonomy/individualism and, 22–24; competence of, 78–79; equality/authority and, 74–75; ethical concerns/students and, 124–126, 128, 129; ethical guidelines for, 17; examples of, 155, 158; full disclosure and, 16, 19; human errors and, 6–13; legal rights of, 109; moral injury and, 3–6; moral outrage and, 13; obedience experiments and, 71–74; review boards and, 136–137, 138, 140, 142, 143, 145; risks/benefits/communication and, 110–114; as a social problem, 2–3; submissive/isolated, 71–74; trust/faith and, 27–28. *See also* Children; Mentally infirm; Patients; Prisoners; Rights of patient/subject
Hyaline membrane disease, 168–169

Hypertension, medication regimen for, 94–95

Illness vocabularies, 86–91
Immunization programs, 11
Impersonal expertise versus caring, 188–190
Incompetence: hospital review committees and, 145–149; licensing boards and, 150–151; malpractice and, 152–153; unreported, 133–135
Informed consent of patient/subject: basic rules for, 108–110; defined, 36; improvements (suggestions) in, 115–119; majority/minority legal rule and, 36–38; patients/full information study (Alfidi) and, 83–84; reasonable man theory and, 38–40. *See also* specific aspects of, e.g., Communication; Human errors; Risks-benefits ratio, etc.
Injury: communication and, 77; legal rule of consent and, 36; probability of, 3, 5
Inmates. *See* Prisoners
Institutional review boards, 135; children as subjects and, 170, 175, 176; defects of, 143; effectiveness of, 140–142; expedited reviews of, 145; history of, 136–139; journal (IRB) for, 140; mentally infirm subjects and, 182–183; prisoner subjects and, 165; recommendations for, 143–145. *See also* Hospital review committees; Peer review committees
Interns: ethical problems and, 127–129; patients' concerns and, 99. *See also* Medical students
Interviews: compliance studies and, 94; importance of consent, 143; patient concerns and, 99, 100; patient memory of, 82–83; physician/patient language difficulties and, 90–91; research admission, 113–114; tape recorded, 110–111
IRB: A Review of Human Subjects, 140
Irwin, John, 162
Ivy Commission, 156

Jacobson, Cardell K., 68–69
James, George, 21
Javits, Senator, 42–43
Joint Commission on Accreditation of Hospitals, 66, 146
Jorgenson, Valerie, 20
Journal of the American Medical Association: language of illness and, 89–90; legalistic fiction of consent and, 10

Karp, Haskell, 45, 48
Katz, Jay, 32, 78
Kefauver, Senator, 42
Kefauver-Harris amendments, 138
Kidney donors: altruism and, 21–22; children as, 174; rationality/communication and, 79–81
Komesar, Neil K., 152–153

Language. *See* Communication; Medical terms
Lasagna, Louis, 117–118
Law: changes/proposed changes and, 45–49; children and, 172–174; consent guide and, 186; limits of, as social control mechanism, 49; medical profession's hostility toward, 33–34; medical records and, 102; medicine and, 41–42; mentally infirm and, 180–181; norms/values and, 33; paternalism/medicine and, 32; professional misconduct, 134; prohibiting nurses from NPSRC, 66–67; risk/consent and, 5; as a set of principles, 32; strong/weak social groups and, 33. *See also* Legal principles; Legal rules
Law-Medicine Research Institute, 137
Legal principles: of battery/negligence, consent and, 35–36, 44; defined, 31–32; generality of, 47–48; independent, 35; norms/values and, 33; in research, 41–45; research/therapy and, 34–35; in therapy, 35–41. *See also* Law; Legal rules

Legal rules: defined, 31–32; generality of, 47–48; informed consent and, 36; injury/consent and, 36; majority/minority, defined, 36–38, 46, 47; minority rule/reasonable man theory and, 39–40; norms/values and, 33; in research, 41–45; research/therapy and, 34–35; social groups and, 33–34; in therapy, 35–41. *See also* Law; Legal principles
License revocation, 134, 151
Licensing boards, 150–152

McIntosh, Jim, 84
Majority rule, informed patient and, 36–38, 46, 47
Malpractice, 35, 43; conspiracy of silence and, 38; *Fortner* v. *Koch* action, 42; new statutes for, 39; nurses and, 69; self-regulation/ethical standards and, 152–153
Marshall, John R., 79, 80
Mastectomy, fear of, 81–82
Mattis, Mary, 126–127
Mead, George Herbert, 115
Mead, Margaret, 56
Mechanic, David, 50–51, 148–149
Medical codes. *See* Professional medical codes
Medical College Aptitude Test (MCAT), 26
Medical ethics, 44, 137; children as subjects and, 171, 172, 176; colleagues/social control and, 129–133; F.D.A./NIH and, 137–138, 139; incompetence and, 135; interns/residents and, 127–129; licensing boards and, 150–151; malpractice and, 152–153; medical students' lack of training in, 124–127; mentally infirm subjects and, 179–180, 184; national commission guidelines for, 17; obligations of researchers and, 119; of peer review and research, 114; research fund decrease and, 25; review board/ethical review and, 136–145; social change and, 190; training in, 124–127, 186. *See also*

Medical ethics (*continued*)
Morality; Professional medical codes
Medical Ethics (Percival), 28
"Medicalization" of society, 55–56
Medical norms, 122; altruism and, 20–22; autonomy/individualism and, 22–24; choices of, 15; defined, 17–18; equality related, 18–20; ethical guidelines and, 17; medical law and, 33; professional codes and, 28–30; rationality/science and, 24–27; sets of, medical dilemmas and, 16; social behavior and, 14–15; as a variable in consent process, 14. *See also* Medical values
Medical records: hospital, available to patient, 103; patient access to, 75, 101–106
Medical relationships: dominance/collegiality models of, 53–61; social controls and, 123
Medical schools: Continuing Medical Education (CME) and, 186; ethical concerns exposure in, 124–127; individualism/physicians and, 23; review boards in, 137; science as a value to investigators and, 26–27. *See also* Medical students; Medical training
Medical Society Ethics Committees, 149–150
Medical students: ethical concerns and, 124–125; ethical training of, 125–127; new rebellious type, 127. *See also* Medical training
Medical terms, patients' difficulty with, 86–91
Medical training: comprehensive care/students and, 99–100; individualism and, 23. *See also* Medical students
Medical values, 122; altruism and, 20–22; autonomy/individualism and, 22–24; choices of, 15; definitions and, 17–18; equality related, 18–20; medical law and, 33; professional codes and changing, 28–30; rationality/science and, 24–27; sets of, medical dilemmas and, 16; social

Medical values (*continued*)
behavior and, 14–15; trust and, 27–28; as a variable in consent process, 14. *See also* Medical norms
Mellinger, Glen, 5
Mentally infirm research subjects, 177–184
Merck, Sharp & Dohme, 155
Milgram, Stanley, 71–73
Miller, Robert, 118–119
Miller, Stephen, 128–129
Millman, Marcia, 147–148
Mills, Don Harper, 135
Minority rule: informed patient and, 36–38, 46, 47; shortcomings of, 39–40
Models of medical relationships. *See* Collegiality model; Dominance model
Moral consensus, authority/legitimacy and, 52
Morality: legalistic fiction of consent and, 10; medical law and, 33; moral autonomy of children, 170–171; moral delinquencies/reporting of, 135; moral injury/experiments and, 3–6; moral outrage and, 13; patient/doctor knowledge of, 55; researchers/individualism and, 23–24; social change and medical, 190; universalism and, 21; values, consent and, 186. *See also* Medical ethics
Moral person, the, 3
Mortality conference, 147–148
Munier, William B., 66
Myocardial infarction, risks/informed patients and, 110–112

Natanson v. *Kline*, 36
National Commission for the Protection of Human Subjects of Biomedical and Behavioral Research, 1, 41, 141; authority/power and, 50–51; basic rules of informed consent and, 109–110; child advocacy of, 167–168, 175, 177; consent reform and, 187; ethical guidelines of, 17;

National Commission (*continued*)
mentally infirm subjects and, 178, 179; moral right/self-determination and, 5; policy for human research, HEW and, 44; prisoner subjects and, 162, 165–166; recommendations/mentally infirm and, 181–184; research/American attitudes and, 25; review board recommendation of, 143–145; special problems and, 155

National Institutes of Health: children as subjects and, 170; drug research and, 137; lack of medical profession's self-regulation and, 189–190; policy statement/human research, 44; review boards and, 138–139; rules for informed consent, 108–110

National Institutes of Mental Health, 179

National Professional Standards Review Council (NPSRC), 66

Negligence. *See* Battery/negligence

Nelson, Benjamin, 21

New England Journal of Medicine, 58, 102

New York State, professional misconduct and, 134, 150

New York State Board of Regents: License revocation and, 134; Southam-Mandel scandal and, 16

Noncompliance, 103; characteristics of patient, 93–94; studies of, 91–99

Nontherapeutic research, children as subjects and, 171–172, 174

Norms, medical. *See* Medical norms

Nunn, Clyde, 25

Nuremberg Code, 29–30, 42, 43, 155, 158, 160, 173

Nurses: conflict with physicians, 66; malpractice suits and, 69; physician incompetence and, 134–135; physicians' improper orders, study of, 67–69; professional dominance of physicians and, 65–69

Obedience experiments, 71–74

"Olympianism," 71

Ombudsmen (hospital), 148, 149

Organ/blood donations, 21–22. *See also* Kidney donors

Pardee, Geraldine P., 113–114

Park, Lee C., 108

Parsons, Talcott, 21, 54, 55, 56, 57

Paternalism, medical law and, 32

Patients: altruism and, 21; autonomy/individualism and, 22–24; autonomy/paternalism, medical law and, 32; clinical, ethical concerns and, 128–129; competence of, 78–79; compliance studies and, 91–99; culpability, 89, 92; equality/authority and, 74–75; as equals, 64; fears of, communication and, 81–82; full disclosure and, 16, 19, 78–79; fully informed, consent and, 83–84; geriatric, Southam-Mandel scandal and, 4, 16, 138; grievance procedures and, 148–149; human errors/consent and, 6–13; interviews, memory of, 82–83; malpractice suits and, 152; medical records and, 101–106; medical terms and, difficulty in understanding, 86–91; moral injury and, 3–6; moral knowledge of, 55, 57; obedience experiments and, 71–74; obligation patterns of, 80; order/compliance attitude of physicians and, 58; physician/researcher accessibility and, 85–86; physician's assumption of ignorance of, 59–61; physician as authoritarian figure to, 61–64; physician's awareness of concerns of, 99–101; as physician's partner, compliance and, 99; primary care, scientific research and, 26; reasonably/sufficiently informed, 36–38; as a social problem, 2–3; submissive/isolated, 71–74; touching of, battery/consent and, 35–36; treatment knowledgeability and, 35; trust/faith and, 27–28; withholding information from, 58–59; women as, 19–20. *See also* Patient's Bill of Rights; Rights of patient/subject

Patient's Bill of Rights, 29; medical records and, 105. See also Rights of patient/subject

Pediatricians: children as subjects and, 175; communication difficulties and, 87–89, 100

Peer review committees, 48; ethics/research and, 114; HEW/human subjects and, 41; medical records and, 104–105. See also Hospital review committees; Institutional review boards

Pepper, Max, 126–127

Perfectionism in communication, 81–83

Personhood: of children, 170–171, 177; of prisoners, 160, 165

Pharmaceutical Manufacturers Association, 157, 158

Pharmacists, compliance and, 95, 98

Phase 1 testing, prisoners and, 157, 158

Physicians: accessibility of, 85–86; altruism and, 22; as authoritarian figure to public, 61–64; battery/negligence, consent cases and, 35–36; "caring" impersonal approach and, 188–190; colleagues/social control and, 129–133; collegiality/dominance models of, 53–61; communication/drug errors in compliance and, 96–99; duty to obtain consent, 48; failure to disclose risk and, 46; fully informing patients and, 83–84; genetic counseling and, 55; hospital performance/review and, 145–149; human errors of/consent and, 6–13; imperialistic ideology of, 60; incompetence in hospitals, 145–149; incompetence and licensing boards, 150–151; incompetence/malpractice and, 152–153; incompetence that goes unreported, 133–135; increased concern for consent and, 35; individualism and, 23; interns/ethical procedures and, 128; majority/minority information jurisdictions and, 36–38; medical records and, 101–106; medical research role of, 11; medical terms,

Physicians (continued)
difficulty in communicating to patient, 86–91; minority legal rule (patient information) and, 38–40; moral injury and, 3–6; moral knowledge of patients and, 55, 57; not listening/patient's description of, 100; nurses and, 65–69; obligation patterns and, 80; order/compliance attitude of, 58; patient competence and, 78–79; patient concerns and, awareness of, 99–101; patient incompetence, attitude of, 59–61; patients as equals and, 64; patients as partners, 99; poor paraprofessional worker relationships of, 59; reasonable man theory of, 38–40, 46; reasonably/sufficiently informed patients and, 36–38; touching of patients/consent suits and, 35–36; trust/faith and, 27–28; women/equality and, 20. See also Researchers; Surgery

Podell, Richard, 95

Polls: antiscientism and, 25; disclosure/treatment refusal and, 19; organ donations and, 22; respect for medicine and, 62

Porterfield, John, 66

Power: abuse of, children and, 175; defined, 52; evidence of patterns in, 61–75; patterns in medical relationships (collegiality/dominance), 53–61; in prison structure, 162–163; social systems/relationships and, 51–53; use of, by professionals, 188

Principles, legal. See Legal principles

Prisoners as research subjects, 155–166

Prison Project of the American Civil Liberties Union, 162

Professional medical codes, 137; changing medical norms/values and, 28–30

Professionals, control/responsibility, 187–188

Psychological research, 11; deception and, 120; obedience experiments and, 71–74

Public Law 93–348, 155

Public opinion polls. See Polls

Quinlan, Karen, 4

Ramsey, Paul, 4
Rand Corporation, 152
Randomized control trials. *See* Controlled trials
Rank, Steven G., 68–69
Rationality: as a medical norm/value, 24–27; special kinds of (kidney transplants, etc.), 79–81
Reasonable man theory, 46; minority rule/reasonably informed patients and, 38–40
Research. *See* Biomedical research
Researchers: accessibility of, 85–86; altruism and, 22; attitude toward consent, 115; attitudes of (science/ethics), 25–27; autoexperimentation and, 27; autonomy/self-regulation, the law and, 34; basic elements of consent and, 108–110; colleagues/social control and, 129–133; consent form composition and, 116–119; deception and, 119–121; dissimulation of, 107; evasions/consent forms and, 109, 111, 114–115; human errors of, consent and, 6–13; individualism and, 23–24; moral injury and, 3–6; review boards and, 139, 142; risks/benefits communication and, 110–114; systematic data and, 12; trust/faith and, 27–28. *See also* Physicians
Research subjects. *See* Human research subjects
Residents: ethical problems and, 127–129; patient's concerns/awareness and, 99. *See also* Medical students
Retarded persons. *See* Mentally infirm
Review boards/committees. *See* Hospital review committees; Institutional review boards; Peer review committees
Rhem, Samuel D., 39
Rights of patient/subject: children's, 167, 173; integrity of physician and, 10; legal, 109; medical records and, 106; mentally infirm, 180; not to be

Rights of patient/subject (*continued*) touched, 35; preemptory right of researcher, 107–108; to be knowledgeable about treatment, 35. *See also* Patient's Bill of Rights
Risks: noncompliance/patient, 93–94; physician's failure to disclose, 46; sufficiently informed patients and, 36–37
Risks–benefits ratio, 23; child subjects and, 177; communication (doctor/patient) and, 77; defined, 3; ethical concerns and, 124, 128; interview, memory of patient and, 82; medical values/norms and, 15; mentally infirm subjects and, 179–180, 182, 183–184; moral weights and, 4–5; research subjects and, 110–114; review boards and, 136, 144–145
Robinson, Daniel, 16
Rubsamen, David S., 47

Sammons, Dr., 151
Scheuneman, Thomas W., 35, 40
Schloendorff v. *Society of New York Hospital,* 36
Schultz, Amelia, 113–114
Schwartz, Shalom H., 21, 22, 79
Schwartz, William B., 152–153
Science: as a medical norm/value, 24–27; medical researchers and, 119
Self-regulation of medical profession, 58, 135, 186; hostility toward the law and, 34; malpractice/ethics and, 152–153; professional use of power and, 188; resistance to/government control and, 189–190
Shenkin, Budd N., 102–106
Shirkey, Harry, 168
Shuy, Roger W., 90–91
Smith, Harmon L., 110–112
Social behavior, medical norms/values and, 14–15
Social change, medical ethics and, 190
Social control, 123, 129–135; formal mechanisms of, 135–152

Social person, the, injury/consent and, 3–5
Social problems: conflict consequences of, 3, 6; defined, 2
Social relationships, 122–123; authority/power and, 51–53
Social systems, authority/power in, 51–53
Sollitto, Sharman, 125
Sorenson, James R., 54, 55, 75
Southam-Mandel scandal, 4, 16, 138
Spodick, David H., 70
Students. *See* Medical students
Subjects. *See* Human research subjects
Surgery: medical authority and innovative, 69–71; patient's memory of interview prior to, 82–83
Survey Research Center, 142, 160, 169–170, 175, 179, 181
Svarstad, Bonnie, 97–99

Tannenbaum, Arnold, 114–115, 142, 143, 163, 164, 176
Thalidomide, 42, 137
Therapeutic privilege, 16, 37, 43
Therapy/treatment: child research subjects and, 168, 171, 174; controlled trials/cardiologists and, 69–70; drug experiments and, 43–44; legal principles/rules and, 34–41; norm/value choices and, 15; patient's right to be knowledgeable about, 35; reasonably/sufficiently informed patients and, 36–38; refusal of/full disclosure and, 19; separating from research, 11; therapeutic privilege and, 16, 37, 43; trust/faith and, 27–28; of the whole person

Therapy/treatment (*continued*) (comprehensive care and communication), 99–101
Titmuss, Richard M., 21
Training. *See* Medical training
Trials. *See* Controlled trials
Trust/faith: based on fiat, 60; as a medical value, 27–28

Vaccarino, James, 48
Values, medical. *See* Medical values
Veatch, Robert, 5, 154; rules of informed consent and, 109–110; teaching ethics and, 125
Vocabularies of illness, communication difficulties and, 86–91
Volunteering: alternatives to, 166; kidney donations and, 21–22; prisoner, 161, 163–164, 166

Waltz, Jon R., 35, 40
Warner, David C., 102–106
Weber, Max, 24
Welt, Louis, 137
Westin, Alan, 17
Willner, Henry S., 118–119
Women: authority/equality and, 75; communication of psychiatric symptoms and, 89; equality and, 19–20; fears of mastectomy and, 81–82; labor-inducing drug/consent study and, 112–113, 131, 140, 175; pediatrician communication and, 87–89, 100; surrogate consent form and, 116

Zerubavel, Eviatar, 85–86

7